MY IVORY CELLAR

BY

JOHN OTT

TWENTIETH CENTURY PRESS, INC.
40 SOUTH CLINTON STREET
CHICAGO 6, ILLINOIS

Symbol of Approval

FULL SPECTRUM

John Ott Laboratories, Inc.

© JOHN OTT

Preface

Shortly after making my first automatic timer and completing several time-lapse sequences of common garden flowers, I began thinking about writing a book on the subject of time-lapse photography. However, there were at that time several minor problems to be ironed out before I could give all the answers, but as each solved problem would create a bigger one, this project was temporarily postponed.

Perhaps this was a mistake, for during the past thirty years the number of unanswered questions has steadily increased and at an ever faster rate. Like so many other subjects, considerable knowledge and experience are required to realize how much more there is still to be learned. This is certainly proving to be true in taking time-lapse pictures.

Although I have exposed a good many feet of motion picture film, I am convinced I have hardly scratched the surface as far as the possible applications of time-lapse photography to all kinds of research projects. It is with this in mind that I am now writing this book to record the information and observations that I feel are worthy of further investigation. It is my sincere hope that the results of some of my time-lapse pictures may be helpful to others engaged in research work, and that by making known as much information as possible, it may narrow the gap still remaining in arriving at the solutions to many unsolved problems.

Contents

Looking in through automatic aluminum shutters of new plastic time-lapse greenhouse at night.

Chapter 1

Time-Lapse Photography

The principle of time-lapse photography is very simple. It is just the opposite of slow-motion pictures, with which most people may be more familiar. In place of slowing fast motion down, it speeds up many times faster than normal such subjects as a flower opening, or the complete growth of a plant on the screen in a few seconds. The actual time represented may have been several months or even years. It is somewhat similar in principle to the animated cartoon type of picture. However, in place of drawing each frame or individual picture to be photographed by hand with the action advanced a little each time, live growing subjects are used. It is then necessary to wait for a little growth to take place between each picture. In some instances, with fairly rapid developing microscopic subjects, this may be only a few seconds. With the opening of the petals of an average flower, it would be about every five or ten minutes, and with something like the development and ripening process of fruit that takes a much longer period of time, it might be one picture every hour or two. The time interval between pictures may have to be changed as the plant goes through different stages of development, such as the opening of a blossom, to the slower maturing process of the fruit. Nevertheless, the individual pictures must be taken regularly throughout the day and night periods.

My first attempt to make a time-lapse picture was in 1927. Although still in high school, this was an outgrowth of an interest in all phases of photography ever since I was old enough to hold a Brownie camera. Some prolonged eye trouble prevented me from reading at times and also made it necessary for me to wear glasses for as long as I can remember. This together with other illness kept me out of school for a considerable period of time. To make a long story short, I did not go to college but

The first step toward a time-lapse studio was the construction of a wooden framework to hold the cameras and lights in addition to the subject being photographed. Note the permanent background behind the subjects and also the metal shutters on window.

began working as a messenger for a stock-brokerage firm the early part of 1929. After the big market crash in October of that same year, the prospects for advancement in that line of business were not exactly what might be considered overwhelming, so I applied for a job with the First National Bank of Chicago. There the opportunity and experience of working in many different departments, including the Investment Division of the Trust Department, Credit and Foreign Departments, the Traveling Audit Department, and finally as an official in the Commercial Loan Department was invaluable. It helped a great deal in better understanding some of the problems of those companies for whom I later made industrial motion picture films. For six years night school kept me busy studying such subjects as Accounting, Money and Banking, Economics, Business Law and English. During the summer of 1937 the bank sent me to the Graduate School of Business Administration, Harvard University, for a special summer course entitled *Interpretation of Financial Statements*. For this I received my first and only diploma during school which I am very proud to say was awarded "with distinction." At no time did my formal education ever include any courses in Botany, Biology, Physics, Electronics, Agriculture, so called health classes or medicine. Maybe this was all for the best in the long run because it left me to solve many problems by trial and error in my own simple way. While working hard at the bank, time-lapse pictures continued as a hobby, and also the making of some regular home movies, including family and travel scenes.

My first time-lapse subject consisted of some apple blossoms brought into the house for early forcing. I knew it would be necessary to take a picture at regular intervals during both the day and night periods but had no idea how frequently it had to be done. I began by hurrying home from school to take a picture every hour for the first day and setting an alarm clock to wake up during the night. By the time the second night rolled around, I thought maybe every two hours would do just as well, and changed my alarm clock accordingly. This business of waking up, turning on the photographic lights, exposing just one frame on the moving picture film, turning off the lights and trying to go back to sleep again became a little monotonous by the third night, and possibly I missed taking one or two of the pictures along toward the early morning hours of the fourth night. When finally completed, the picture turned out far from perfect, in fact the blossoms opened so rapidly on the screen it was almost impossible to see the motion at all—there was the bud and then all of a sudden it was wide open.

This first experiment was disappointing, of course, but it did prove one thing—namely, that it was necessary to take individual pictures more frequently and over a much longer period of time if the final results were to show the gradual growth and development of the flowers. It was also obvious that I would have to build an automatic machine to take the pictures for me, as it frequently was a little awkward to run home every hour to take another picture. As I recall, it was during history class at school one day that the idea came to me as to how I would build a contraption to operate the camera automatically. To start with, I borrowed the works from the kitchen clock and made my first timer, which still is operating today. It always has been my intention to put the works back in the old kitchen clock when I am finished, but that time never seems to come.

Original kitchen clock timer showing face of kitchen clock mounted in center of bakelite panel. Flat triangular head pins are used for electrical contacts. Specially bent paper clip is used in place of hands to make contact. An extra flat head pin is mounted opposite each numeral to hold paper clip back until spring tension is sufficient to snap past and make firm contact on second pin. When small toggle switch opposite each numeral is turned toward center, timer will operate camera as paper clip hand goes by. If switch is turned away from center, then timer will not operate.

Basically a timer for this purpose should have two circuits: one to turn the lights on and off, and the other to trip the

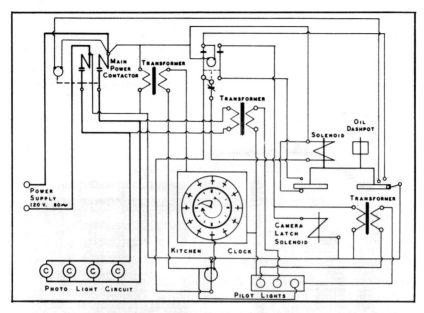

Electrical wiring diagram for original kitchen clock timer.

camera. It should also have some provision for adjusting the time interval. When I first started taking time-lapse pictures, the village blacksmith shop was still in existence, and the blacksmith was a great help. However, there was also a new machine shop, and a young machinist, named Herman Schubert, helped me with some of the more intricate parts. He has since built much of the special equipment, including my new automatic plastic greenhouse, and also most of the equipment I now use for taking microscopic time-lapse pictures.

In order to have an even amount of light, and of the same consistent color value, it is necessary to shut out the daylight and turn on the same number of electric lights for each picture. Then the exposure will be the same day and night and on cloudy and bright days. Otherwise the picture would flicker badly. At first I used a small electric motor with a wide pulley wheel that simply wound up the window shade cord and stalled when it was completely closed. The catch had to be removed from the roller shade so the spring would wind it back up and unwind the cord from the pulley when the current went off again. A little experimenting in balancing the motor power against the spring tension in the roller shade soon had everything working fine. For an ordinary window shade a two-inch diameter pulley wheel and a one-tenth horse-power motor is about right. This motor of course should be connected to the same electric circuit as the lights, and of a type that will not overheat when stalled. This roller shade idea of stalling the electric motor always horrified any real engineer, but it was simple, inexpensive, and it worked.

Its principle drawback was that the pull-cord wore out rather quickly, and occasionally broke before I could replace it. The shade slammed closed and rolled back up again with a rather loud noise. This used to wake up some of the lighter sleepers in the house who did not have the full understanding and appreciation of the basic problems involved in time-lapse photography. On two occasions the police stopped in to investigate what they thought had been some sort of explosion, or bomb going off. That of course would wake up everybody during the middle of the night, including some of the neighbors. Fortunately the roller shades have long since been replaced with more positive-acting and silent shutters that close smoothly and evenly by air pressure. They also stay closed at night, so the bright photographic lights no longer light up the whole neighborhood.

Various safety features and alarm signals have more recently been added so that if the photographic lights remain on for more than thirty seconds, a gong rings under my bed and an indicator on an annunciator board shows where the trouble is. If the temperature in the studio goes beyond the predetermined maximum or minimum, the gong rings and the annunciator board signals the difficulty. Other possible trouble such as the sump pump not working or the electric power going off will immediately ring the gong and show on the signal board. This system works from electric batteries so will not be affected by failure of the public service power.

Finding certain subject material to photograph was not always easy. Usually I tried growing the subjects myself. Sometimes they could be obtained from a local florist or ordered from some nurseryman's catalog. The latter was the case with a paw-paw tree. After searching through many catalogs, I finally found this item listed. The small trees arrived with bare roots the following spring, and I planted them with great care. One or two small leaves came out, but all the trees were soon dead. I re-ordered three more trees for delivery the following spring and requested that the roots be dug with a ball of dirt and wrapped in burlap. These trees put forth a few more leaves than the first ones did, but by mid-summer they too had all died. Then I wrote to the nurseryman and told him of my experience and asked him for suggestions. He promptly replied that he had never been able to transplant these trees successfully, and he knew of no one else who had done it, but would be glad to continue shipping them as long as anyone continued to order them. He did volunteer the information that he had started all his trees from seed quite some years ago, but of course this method would require considerable time to grow a tree of any size.

My first encounter with any medical subjects came through an older friend of mine (middle-aged), who lived next door. He had graduated as a doctor, and was specializing in surgery, as well as teaching at the old Rush Medical School in Chicago. He asked me to make some moving pictures of different operations so he could show them to the students in his classes. He was on night emergency call at County Hospital, so this worked out fine for both of us. During one operation the film ran out in the middle of the most important part, so the picture had to be finished at another time. This film always caused considerable comment, as the patient became so pale during the operation. The first man was a negro, and the second was white.

About this same time I made my first microscopic time-lapse pictures of a medical subject, which came about as a result of an entire family being brought into the hospital, stricken with trichinosis. They all had eaten a home-butchered pig without proper inspection or knowledge of the dangers involved. These pictures showed the trichinae going through various stages of development.

Several years later it was my honor to be asked to serve on the Board of Directors of the North Shore Country Day School, in Winnetka, Illinois. At one of the meetings the fact came up for discussion that a boy of mine in the school didn't think much of some of the class-room films he had seen. I went over to see one once, and was inclined to agree with him whole-heartedly. After being challenged to do something about it, I decided to

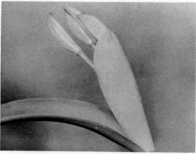

Formation of the sheath containing buds of the cattleya orchid.

Enlarged buds ready to burst into bloom.

Flower buds are shown as they break through the sheath.

The orchid flowers are almost in full bloom.

Buds are starting to burst open.

Orchid plant in full bloom. (Exposures first at 30-minute intervals, later every 5 minutes.)

First microscopic time-lapse equipment consisted of a 35 mm moving picture camera and microscope coupled together with special split beam prism eye piece assembly. Microscope at right is equipped with an attachment for making still pictures. Both microscopes are mounted on wooden base with thermostat and light blubs to provide heat. Entire assembly was covered with insulated wooden box with glass top in order to control temperature.

undertake the making of a class-room instructional film. This certainly was a new experience. My boy who was responsible for getting me into this situation was in fifth grade, and seemed to be having some difficulty in arithmetic with fractions. This was as good a subject as any, so the film was entitled WHAT ARE FRACTIONS?

A fellow named Grant Evans had previously done some camera work for me. He had a friend interested in such things, so between us we came up with a completed film for fifth grade students, intended to explain what fractions are. The plot was not so exciting as a mystery or a Western, but did seem to get the idea across to fifth graders as to just what a fraction is. It dealt primarily with someone sawing a piece of two-by-four into various pieces of equal size. All the pieces were then neatly placed beside the lower portion or denominator to show that this part of the fraction indicated into how many parts the piece of wood had been cut. Then a hand lifted out several pieces at a time and placed them alongside of the numerator to indicate how much of the entire piece of wood the top part or numerator represented. Thus, the fifth graders could visually see just what two-fifths or seven-eighths of a piece of wood was. The same idea was repeated with other objects, and simple as this was, it seemed to get across to the fifth graders a clear idea of what fractions are in a matter of ten minutes. This film received some sort of an award, and has since been used by quite a few schools in cities around the country. Next came a request for thirty more class-room films from one of the largest class-room film distributors in the country to make a complete series on arithmetic. The only catch was that while they liked the first film on fractions, they felt that there should be a board of twelve professors to advise on and approve of the scripts. If you ever want some different opinions on simple fundamentals of fifth grade arithmetic, all you need is a group of experts on the subject. That finished it right then and there.

The success of my original film on fractions was due largely to its simplicity, and this was a good fundamental rule that I always tried to remember and apply when attempting to make films later on of more complicated subjects.

Soon after this, a representative of the O. M. Scott & Sons Company, grass seed and lawn care products, stopped at the house one day and asked if I was the fellow that made time-lapse pictures. O. M. Scott and Company wanted a film on the subject of lawn care, including the effects of 2-4 D the new weed killer. This was my first attempt to make a commercial film. Among other things the pictures showed that instead of stimulating the weeds so that they grew so fast they died from over-exhaustion, as was the common story going around, that 2-4 D acted as a poison and caused a distorted and slowing down of the growth rate until the weed gradually died. Another similar picture showing the roots of plants growing against a sloping glass plate clearly indicated they followed a normal pattern and would not alter their established direction of growth to seek out either plant food or moisture. Roots that did reach plant food or moisture developed larger and stronger, but there was absolutely no indication of any other roots changing their normal pattern of growth. This was directly contrary to the generally accepted theory, but then my time-lapse cameras never went to

Young corn plant showing roots, growing in different types of soil and plant food and against sloping glass so that growth results may be studied.

college either. Various other industrial companies made similar requests that necessitated getting more cameras especially adapted for time-lapse work. Soon I had four cameras set up under a special skylight built over an ordinary basement window areaway.

In connection with these films it was occasionally necessary to say a few words at some meeting or after dinner group. No one could have felt more awkward doing this so I decided to take a course in public speaking. The course was helpful, but the only way to get over this stage fright, or uneasy feeling, was just to go out and do more public speaking. Several local groups—the Garden Club, American Legion, Thursday Night Men's Club at the church, and others—asked me to show my time-lapse pictures, and each time it became a little easier to tell about them. Before long I had other requests, and began charging a regular fee. There is no doubt that this makes people appreciate any program more. They put forth more effort to make the event a success. Many people seem to think a free program isn't worth attending. It was quite pleasing to find how many people enjoyed watching the time-lapse pictures, and with each showing there would be two or three more requests. I tried to arrange for a regular booking agent to handle the necessary correspondence and other details, but no one was interested in handling a lecture on just flowers. Finally I picked a name out of a hat and had some letterheads printed as "The Midwest Lecture Bureau." My secretary, Miss Clara Wright, took charge and handled everything for me on a very official and businesslike basis.

Sometimes the facilities for darkening the lecture hall were not always the best. Occasionally it was necessary to wait until after dark outside before starting the pictures. Whenever this was necessary, the story about ordering the paw-paw trees helped fill time. If necessary, I could go on to explain that the following year a garden club lady sent me seeds that did sprout and grow very nicely. Two years later though a part-time temporary helper was weeding the garden and border where the paw-paws were growing. He was a very thorough and conscientious worker, and that was the end of my effort to grow paw-paw trees.

Another good story for filling time while waiting for the sun to set had to do with ordering some special soil from North

Carolina. It had a high leaf mold content on the acid side for growing certain bog plants. To start with, 50 pounds were ordered on a trial basis. However, the telephone connection was not very good, and the man in North Carolina loaded 50 tons in two railroad gondola cars which arrived as somewhat of a surprise. This made a considerably bigger pile of dirt in the back yard than planned for, but provided the means for many interesting experiments. Many plants, shrubs and trees considered not hardy in the Chicago climate grew and flowered very well when they were in their native soil in spite of weather conditions.

In observing the growth of plants, I noticed that the flowers and leaves always faced into the light and that the leaves noticeably drooped from lack of water, but would quickly revive when given a drink. I always placed the camera so that the constant daylight came from behind and thus the flowers in facing the daylight would also be facing directly into the camera.

One night I dreamed up a wild idea of controlling the light, temperature and moisture to make the leaves of the plants move in different directions. To accomplish this, it was necessary to construct special flower pots that would move around on wheels. In each pot was place a small electric heating element and a water tube. Many different flowering plants were tested and primroses found to respond the best to this treatment. A few more refinements on my timing contraption and everything was all set. The flower pots were pulled around on a track like an old fashioned cable car, but at a speed of about ½ inch an hour. The heating elements were turned on at the proper time to wilt the leaves down and the plants were given just the proper amount of water to revive them again. A battery of lights was turned on one side and then the other which would attract the leaves from side to side. Thus it was possible to move the plants around a miniature stage and control both the up and down motion and also sideward motion of the leaves. It only remained to synchronize this motion to music. This sequence lasted only two minutes on the screen but required five years to complete, including an interruption of two years while I was in the Navy. This interruption caused a few blank frames on the film which went by much faster on the screen than it seemed to while I

Original kitchen clock timer with a few more additional attachments added in order to make pictures of waltzing primroses.

was gone. These dancing primroses always caused considerable comment, and later I used them as the opening theme for all my television programs.

Obtaining some of the necessary electrical equipment for the dancing primroses was often a problem too, especially following the war period while priorities were still in force. Everybody always wanted to know why I needed a particular type of switch and what I intended doing with it. At first I tried to avoid any direct reference to the waltzing primroses but was always given some excuse for a further delay in delivery of the equipment needed. Finally one day I told the manager of the sales department of a particular company that I had to have a certain automatic switch in order to take pictures of my dancing primroses doing a Strauss waltz. It was hard to keep a straight face. This certainly was a reason the sales manager had not heard of before. He must have thought the easiest and quietest way to get rid of me was to let me have the switch.

Making the pictures of the dancing flowers tied up the use of most of my time-lapse cameras for the full five years. Other work had to be done also. The only solution was to enlarge the time-lapse studio. The logical location was to extend the present basement window area-way out into my wife's rose garden. This would have access from the basement and provide a suitable location for a skylight. After it was built some of the roses were put right back where they had been growing and everything leveled off nice and smooth again.

About this same time the storage of all the completed time-lapse pictures was becoming an increasingly acute problem. With some reluctance my wife turned over the remainder of a little space in a basement closet where she had been keeping jams and similar supplies. The constant temperature and humidity of the jam closet was ideal for storage of film. Not long afterwards the chicken coop proved to be an ideal location for an editing room, so out went the roosts to make way for all the film editing equipment. The garage was just the right size for a small sound recording studio which made it rather hard on the old family car, especially during cold mid-winter weather. The front lawn and flower gardens sometimes looked like a patch work quilt from testing various fertilizers, weed killers and other garden products, but my wife still steadfastly refuses to give up a small corner of the laundry and one of the tubs for a dark room.

Showing my films and talking to many different groups of people was not only an enjoyable experience and made speaking

My wife's jam closet made the most ideal location for storing film. The temperature and humidity were just right the year round.

publicly much easier but also taught me several lessons about what not to say. At one large convention I was one of several speakers. The program was a little behind schedule, and those in charge were trying to hurry things along. To be as brief as

After doing weekly half-hour TV programs live in Chicago, 60 were repeated at home and recorded on film. A similar set was built in the garage. The walls and roof were sound-proofed. Lights, cameras and recording equipment were moved in which made it rather hard on the old family car especially during the winter months.

possible, I cut my introductory remarks short and suggested we start the film, as one picture was as good as ten thousand words. The next speaker was a prominent United States Senator who apologized for not having any pictures but promised to hurry through his ten thousand words.

At the back of this book is a list of some of the organizations and places where I had the privilege of showing my films and meeting many wonderful people—people who have told me many interesting things about plants and flowers, and people who gave me many very helpful suggestions and ideas. I made many friends and acquaintances that I will never forget. Maybe some one reading this book will remember the guy with the time-lapse pictures.

In most instances I gave only one lecture a day, but frequently two; and, as I remember, the record was four lectures in one day in different cities, covering a total distance of two hundred miles. The more I showed my films in different parts of the country, the more requests kept coming in, and also more requests to have time-lapse pictures made. In fact, it was becoming more and more obvious that time-lapse photography was interfering with banking, or possibly banking was interfering with taking time-lapse pictures. The days (and nights) just weren't long enough even with bankers' hours to get everything done that I wanted to do.

This was a difficult decision, as I really enjoyed the work at the bank. Besides, my father and grandfather had worked there, and my uncles and a cousin or two. I had worked there myself almost twenty years; so it was quite a well-established family tradition. Time-lapse photography was all right maybe as a hobby, but surely no one in his right mind would ever try anything so unconventional, so uncertain, so unheard of in lieu of banking. I can still hear one old-timer in the bank explaining that I was leaving in order to have more time to take pictures of African violets and apple blossoms. There are both advantages and some disadvantages to following in all the family's footsteps, but there are also times when it is a great relief that my grandfather never made any time-lapse pictures.

Chapter 2

Further Afield in Photography

When I first began taking time-lapse pictures strictly as a hobby, it did not matter too much if a certain flower bloomed or not. There were plenty of others that could easily be substituted and only the best pictures used. In fact a pretty good definition of an expert photographer is a fellow who has learned not to show his poor pictures. However, as requests for time-lapse pictures of specific plants or flowers were received, it was necessary to try and solve each individual flower's problem. At first some seemed to act like a temperamental prima donna with a deep psychological disturbance, but sooner or later a basic biological cause for their misbehavior would become evident. In some cases this was purely accidental, and in others the results proved just the opposite from what I had expected. One great advantage was the wide range of subjects to be photographed. One day I would be photographing the techniques of hybridizing oat flowers, in order to develop new disease resistant varieties. The next day might be the study of a new type of electrode in an electric furnace, the budding of yeast for the brewery industry, the demonstration of heavy mining machinery, or the effects of a new antibiotic drug on some microscopic disease causing organism. In order to make an interesting and intelligent moving picture on any subject, it was first necessary to understand something about the subject to be photographed. In some instances I worked jointly with the top research personnel of many large companies and university research scientists. Accordingly, I had an invaluable education in a rather round-about way.

In addition to the time-lapse pictures of the subjects under direct study, many of these people suggested other subjects of interest for time-lapse pictures to be taken in my spare time. What impressed me most was how so many apparently unrelated subjects began to fit together into an overall pattern and would respond to similar treatments in much the same way.

One summer my schedule of lectures and picture taking took me to all corners of the country and in between points as well. On one trip to Paricutin volcano my wife and I flew to Mexico City, drove on good roads 300 miles west, and transferred to an old jalopy that could travel better over the rocks and bumps of the back roads. When the jalopy could go no further, we rode mules over jagged lava flows that were still rather uncomfortably hot. The last few miles had to be on foot, as the terrain was even too rough for a mule. As soon as we reached a good high place from which to take pictures, our guide was ready to return. He couldn't understand why anyone would want to spend the day in such a place and wait until dark just to take night scenes of the fiery lava flows and giant explosions of molten lava. Perhaps it was the evil spirits of the volcano that frightened him, but nothing would persuade him to wait with us. He departed, and we stayed on by ourselves. It was quiet and peaceful except for one or two violent explosions that belched molten lava and rocks high into the air. The accompanying sudden and terrifically loud noises seemed to literally shake the earth and almost made both of us jump out of our skins. My wife still refers to that day as one of the most beautiful and peaceful days we have ever had together just sitting by the volcano taking pictures on into the night.

In the distant moonlight could be seen the steeple of a church that was all that was left of a town of 10,000 inhabitants. Here were lava flows in the making. In the still of the night could be heard an echo of the days of Pompeii, Mount Pelee and Kilauea. I thought of the verse from the BIBLE, "In the beginning God created the heaven and the earth." (Genesis 1:1) ". . . and every living creature that moveth . . . and He saw that it was good." (Genesis 1:21) "But forget not this one thing, beloved, that one day is with the Lord as a thousand years, and a thousand years as one day." (II Peter 3:8) "For a thousand years in thy sight are but as yesterday when it is past, and as a watch in the night." (Psalms 94)

These quotations from the Bible in regard to the creation of the earth, emphasize that a day to the Lord is many years in comparison to man's day, and must be thought of as representing an infinite period of time rather than twenty-four hours. The many years required for the creation of the earth as seen in the eyes of man are as but a few days to the Lord.

As the flaming lava continued to erupt from the crater, I began to think of what the earth might have been like millions of years ago. Where did it come from? What was it like before the earth and the sun and stars and the moon as we know them today came into existence? Could some of the similar principles of growth response in different plants and animals all stem from the same original source of the first primitive life on our earth? Originally there must have been a vast expanse of space reaching out in all directions beyond anything we today can comprehend or even imagine—infinite space. My guess is that in all this space there was nothing—nothing but a plan—but a very definite over-all plan of events that were to take place throughout time to come, a plan for the creation of the earth and the sun and the stars and the moon, and a plan for the creation of that miracle called "Life."

One theory is that great clouds of various gases made their appearance out of nowhere and began drifting toward one another with ever-increasing speed. Vast charges of static electricity were created, and suddenly, with the fury of a gigantic tornado, they began whirling around and around. As they traveled on through space, they whirled faster and faster, thus creating the force of gravity. Gradually, as this force grew stronger, the outer extremities of this whirling mass began to draw in toward the center. Pressure developed, and with this pressure came heat, pressure and heat so terrific that finally the entire mass burst into flame, and continued to burn for millions of years more. Slowly it began cooling down as vast amounts of heat were radiated off into space. Maybe the earth and other planets in our universe were small parts of the sun cast off by centrifugal force, or pulled away from the central mass by the gravity of a passing star so that they could cool down much faster than the main body of the sun. Maybe each was created separately along with all the other stars in the heavens, but it does seem certain that our earth has gradually cooled down from a great concentration of burning gas—cooled down to a

ball of red hot molten mineral and rock. The outer surface has
continued to cool and form a solid crust which shriveled and
cracked and heaved as this cooling and shrinking process went
on for many more millions of years.

Luckily though, all the original gases that went into this con-
glomeration did not mix into one single element, but instead,
retained their original identity so that today we have many different minerals, without which life could not exist. Luckily also,
these gases did not all liquefy and solidify at the same temperature, but instead, some still remained in their gaseous form, so
we have the air we breathe. Some, within today's present range
of temperatures, are liquid, and we have water; while others
have turned to solid, and we have rock—the very earth itself—
rock containing different minerals that make them all the colors
of the rainbow. Some are yellow, some white, others black,
others red.

Could all this be just luck or happenstance, or is it a part of
an over-all plan? Luck or planned, the progress of development
continued. The air carried moisture from the oceans to fall as
rain over the solid rocks, to form lakes, large and small, and
to form rivers that flow from all parts of the land, swirling and
churning as the waters rush on, eroding the rocks and carrying
minute particles of all the different minerals that originally
went into this earth of ours, down from the mountains, through
the valleys, and back into the ocean again. The wind made
waves and the moon created tides. Ocean currents continued to
churn the waters until finally the exact mixture of minerals and
chemicals came together with an impact that created the greatest
miracle of all—life—a single cell, but a living cell, a minute
plant that could eat and live and grow. It could create more living cells by the simple process of dividing in two, each part
continuing to grow—for it contained life.

But this single little cell, the simplest form of life, also contained some of the most complicated mysteries that still remain
unsolved. They are the chromosomes and genes that contain the
hereditary characteristics and instinctive impulses that have
controlled the development of all other forms of life. While
these cells continued to multiply and create millions of other
single cells exactly alike and are still doing so today, somewhere,

somehow a change took place so that some cells grouped together and began to form plants of different shapes and characteristics. As time passed, further great strides forward came one after another as plants developed separate parts that were each dependent on the other for existence, such as roots, stems, and leaves—leaves of all shapes and sizes—but regardless of shape or size, the primary function of the leaf is to utilize the power radiated from the sun to combine air and water with minerals taken from the ground by the plant's root system and convert these into food energy that supports all life on this world.

Suddenly another. terrific explosion and the upheaval of more fiery lava startled me. I came back with a jolt to the reality of the present. The mules were waiting to take us back to the jalopy so we could start our journey home.

Many of our other trips were made by auto all the way, and some of our children accompanied us most of the time. We visited almost all the national parks, and by the end of the summer thought we had seen quite a bit of God's country. As might be expected, I took a camera or two and a few miscellaneous accessories along in the car. We drove from Chicago to the West Coast and back twice. One trip included motoring from Southern California up the Coastal Highway to the Canadian border. In addition to going back and forth across the country, we also went up and down from the top of Pikes Peak to the bottom of Death Valley. We went below ground to see Carlsbad Cavern, and on another trip we fought the rapids of Hell's Canyon up the swift current of the Snake River.

One of the most memorable trips included a ride on muleback down to the bottom of the Grand Canyon in Arizona. Probably no place in the world presents a more interesting resume of the earth's history than can be seen written in the rocks of this region—rocks of all colors and character. The dark rocks at the bottom of the Canyon were formed during the first period of geological time; rocks that have been twisted and bent under great heat and pressure, and in which no evidence of life has ever been found. Above these are rocks of the second geological period of history, and show less bending and twisting, but contain traces of some of the earliest forms of plant life. With each additional stratum of rock new and higher forms of both land and marine life are evident, for everywhere can be seen rocks of different origin, some from the drifting sands of pre-historic times, the sediments of ancient seas, the deposits from early rivers, as well as great flows of lava; all of which tell a story of changing conditions and climate, the formation and erosion of rock and the story of life itself that existed during these early periods of time.

The experience of seeing many of the wonders of our national parks is an education in itself. Our National Park Service has certainly done a wonderful job in pointing out all the places of interest and supplying helpful information, all sorts of further, apparently unrelated, bits of information, that kept tying into other pictures of totally different subjects that I will try and piece together further on in this book.

Chapter 3

The Steady and Orderly Evolution of Plants

The geological story of the earth's origin is fascinating, but the steady progress in the development of plants from the most primitive to the more complex forms is almost unbelievable. There are plants that react fast enough to catch flies for food and plants that produce true eggs instead of seeds. Nature seems to have experimented in many ways in formulating the laws or rules for plant growth. But for each rule there seems to be some exception or new experiment, and one of the best examples of this is the ordinary banana plant. This plant produces fully developed and mature fruit without the flowers being pollinated. It is known as a parthenocarpic plant and should not be confused with a self-pollinating type of flower. The banana flower is male sterile and produces no pollen at all. The seeds except for some very rare exceptions are not viable. This is a great handicap to the fruit companies that raise bananas, as it therefor has not been possible to improve the present varieties of bananas through hybridization as is commonly done with many other fruits, flowers and vegetables. Certain insects, crustaceans, and worms are also known to reproduce by means of development from an unfertilized egg. Some plants produce both spores and seeds, and some animals lay eggs but are part mammal. Sounds confusing, but all seems to fit together into the overall pattern for the steady progress and development of life on our earth.

The first plant life is thought to have started in the sea in the warm tropical waters where the temperature remains quite constant. From these sunny climates started the march of plants to cover the earth with their green mantle as we see it today.

The most interesting part of the Venus fly trap is the trap on the end of each leaf.

On each flat surface of the trap are three tiny hair-like bristles that act as triggers. Insect must touch one bristle twice or two bristles each once in quick succession to spring trap.

Fly entering trap. Notice toes of fly on foot against one of the spines at edge of trap. Plant also secretes a nectar on surface of trap that attracts fly and also drugs it to retard reactions.

Fly has sprung trap which is closing about it. Trap snaps closed in approximately ½ second.

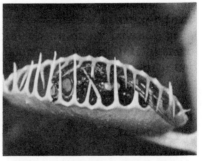

Fly firmly caught in grip of fly trap. Plant digests food value contained in insect within a day or two. Trap then opens again.

The sporocarp of the clover leaf fern is about the size of a small garden pea.

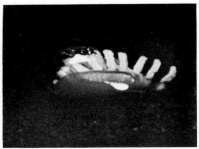

Water makes the sporocrap swell and burst open releasing true egg masses.

A gelatin substance holds the egg masses intact. Slowly this substance dissolves releasing a few eggs at a time.

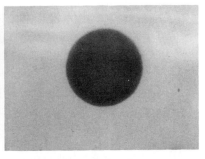

Microscopic view of sperm case also released by sporocarp. 4,000 magnification.

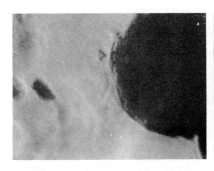

Sperm cases burst open releasing sperms that swim with their own motion to radar antennae like plate at end of egg.

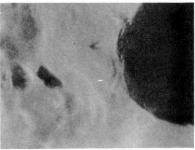

After making contact, sperm reverses action and backs away from egg.

A big step forward was the emergence of plants out of the sea to take root on dry land and adapt themselves to varying conditions. This was a gradual step that required many more millions of years, but it went on slowly and deliberately. From the first plants that fringed the oceans where they were constantly splashed by waves and covered by the tide, remaining out of the water for short periods at a time, the first strictly land plants began to grow. One of the most primitive strictly land plants is the lichen.

Lichens are a combination of a fungus and an alga, and together, this combination accomplished feats that neither can do by itself. Both fungi and algae are two of the world's oldest forms of plants, and lived on the earth for millions of years before the thread-like growth of the fungus started to grow around the green cell of the algae. This new combination was thus created—something that has never happened elsewhere in the world of plant or animal life.

There are many varieties of lichens, but their characteristics are the same. They are one of the slowest growing plants in the world, but also the most widely distributed. A single plant one inch in diameter might be fifty or more years old. These very small plants have microscopic hairlike roots that secrete an acid that actually dissolves the rock as they grow. The roots of lichens have been known to penetrate as much as half an inch into solid rock. When rocks have been covered with lichens, they will crumble easily compared to bare rock. Thus these most primitive plants hasten the weathering and decomposition of rocks producing soil for other plants to come.

From the earliest invention of cell-division plants that came out of the oceans, the process of further development began. In some unexplained way, new and more complicated forms of plants appeared. These were the first spore plants, such as the mosses, ferns and horsetails. A spore is a single cell that drops from the parent plant or is carried by the wind to a new location. Wonderful as this new development was, the spore had its shortcomings, as it was vulnerable to the adversities of weather and climates. Spores will grow well, provided the moisture conditions are just right, but in this respect alone, the spore was limited as to where these plants could travel. In the swamps and marshes where conditions were right, the growth of the spore plants was unusually prolific. Club mosses and horsetails grew to one hundred feet or more in height. Tree ferns were common. The lush green growth of these spore plants, the most luxuriant growth the world has ever seen, was at its height two hundred million years ago. This era continued for a hundred million years. A hundred million years is quite a long time even geologically speaking, and while these plants continued to grow, developing great jungle-like forests of giant horsetails, club mosses and tree ferns, other events of tremendous importance were also taking place.

A few types of primitive creatures had begun to move around in the waters. The amoeba was one of the first single-celled animals that could change its shape by putting forth long lobes, and in this way could move about. It could also envelop other microscopic particles and slowly absorb them for food. The amoeba, like the first plants, also reproduced by cell division. Then, just as plant cells grouped together, so did animal cells. Tentacles developed that could reach out for food. But also, these animals developed a new method of reproduction. Instead of dividing in half, they developed a form of budding. Here a sort of bud starts growing, which finally breaks off and continues to grow. Next, other microscopic creatures that did not look much different from some of the early plants began to move much faster. But through the disciplined process of creation, step by step, just as plants had developed their roots, stems, and leaves, some of these little creatures, after hundreds of thousands of generations, began to look different. They had little whip-like paddles and could move about still faster—but this movement required much more energy, and to supply this energy fast enough, a radically new system of eating and digesting food had to be developed. Here was something entirely new and different—another great stride forward. But things did not stop now. The little paddles continued to develop into more streamlined fins, and with this greater speed and necessity for food, came eyes, gills, a skeleton structure of bone, and above all, a brain to regulate these radically new innovations of life. The brain and its intricate nervous system, primitive as it was in this early form of fish life, was truly a marvel of creation to behold.

Here again, different forms and shapes of fish appeared. Nature was generous with color—all sorts of color combinations—some were red, some yellow, others black, or plain white.

Just as plant life came out of the oceans, also out of the oceans came animal life. Not over night—not in a year, but again through the changes that took place through the force of time. How did this happen? The pioneer that led this land invasion was an ancient ancestor of our present day scorpion. It was able to become an air breather because of its exceedingly simple "book lungs," which needed only slight modification to become efficient users of oxygen. Perhaps, too, the Egyptian Lung Fish had something to do with this transition, for the story is that those fish would be stranded on the dry land when the Nile receded after each flood. Many were trapped, and perished as the water dried up, so finally they developed lungs in addition to their gills. Then, as the waters receded, they would roll themselves up in a ball of mud to await the next annual flood. Meanwhile, in more modern times, the Egyptian natives have become wise to this and collect these balls of mud, breaking them open as necessary to provide fresh fish dinners throughout the year. There are still many animals today that begin life under water. The frog starts as a tadpole. Many insects, like the mosquito, develop from little wrigglers in the water. The dragon-fly is another.

While the appearance of early forms of fish and insects during the era of spore plants naturally had its significance in later developments, the spore plants themselves, that were growing at this time, play an important part in our modern civilization today, for it was the layer upon layer of these early plants that grew and fell, building up the deposits of plant material that was to be compressed during the next two hundred million years into coal.

Today fossils of some of these early plants reveal important information, and one example was brought to light in Gilboa, New York, when a flash flood raced down out of the Catskill Mountains in 1869, washed away the old river bed, and uncovered some petrified tree stumps. These stumps were of tree ferns three to four feet in diameter and were standing right where they had grown three hundred million years ago. The important information revealed was that these early tree ferns had produced some primitive forms of seeds in addition to spores. The age of these petrified trees is determined by the kind of stone and rock they are found in. At Saratoga, New York, an outcropping of stone laid down five hundred million years ago reveals an unsolved mystery. Curious shaped objects that have turned to stone have rings like tree rings, but, according to all present theories, these strange things grew two hundred million years before there were supposed to have been any land plants. Were these some of nature's first underwater experiments with the type of growth or development of layer over layer as later used in modern trees—developed under water like everything else, and raised up into the hills millions of years after they had turned into stone?

While we are on the subject, the great petrified forest of Arizona is an excellent example of plants and trees that have turned to stone. It was formed during the period that immediately followed the time when our coal was being made.

In the Arizona desert at an elevation of over 5,000 feet is the greatest concentration of petrified wood known in the world. It is not plain stone, but actually agate, jasper, opal, and onyx, formed by the wood pulp slowly being replaced by minerals in the water that seeped into the wood and hardened. These giant trees, consisting of 39 different species, include ferns, cycads, horsetails, pines, and ginkgos, and are thought to have floated down rivers and lodged in their present location, which then was a lush and fertile semi-tropical valley at sea level. Also in a remote section of Arizona, is the footprint of a dinosaur left in the mud of a river bank, long since turned into stone.

While the great coal-making era was dominated by spore plants, we have seen that even prior to this time nature had experimented with some of the first early forms of seeds, but it was not until after the great swamps dried up that development of seeds really got under way. Maybe nature was put to it to find other ways to propagate plants as the conditions prevailing in the warm moist swamps changed to those of wind swept hills. Apparently development of seeds was already under way so that plants could travel to the regions beyond where the first spore plants grew. One of the earliest seed plants was the

cycad, which still flourishes today, but principally in the southern hemisphere. It is a step halfway between a fern and a palm,
but it does produce seeds. These early types of seeds are called
"naked" seeds, and grow on an exposed stalk. As they ripen,
they merely fall directly to the ground beneath. Instead of a
single cell spore, they are a complete embryo of a new plant,
supplied with a quantity of concentrated food and all wrapped
up in a weather-proof covering, so they can retain their spark
of life over long periods of drought or cold weather, and be
ready to sprout when the right time comes.

Another early experiment with seed trees was the ginkgo
which grows principally in the northern hemisphere. This tree
almost went into extinction along with some of the trees of the
petrified forest, and others known today only through their fossils. The ginkgo is a transition in the evolution to pine, the next
step forward. It is a combination of fern, pine and true hardwood all in one. Its pollen is similar to that of a fern, its wood
structure is like that of pine, and its broad leaves suggest a
fore-runner of the hardwood trees to come. An interesting fea-
ture of the more modern hardwood trees is that their sapwood
grows in such a way that the cells form little pipe-lines through
which the sap flows, compared to the sapwood of soft wood trees,
which filters the sap through the walls of the cells from one
to another.

The pine was the first of the true coniferous soft wood trees.
Moreover, its seeds represented a big improvement over those
of the cycads which grew in the open on the end of the seed
stalk, and merely dropped to the ground when ripe. There were
no squirrels or birds yet to steal the seeds, but there were some
primitive reptiles that might have eaten them. If pine trees
were to spread out to dominate the plant world, they must have
more seed and some kind of protection so they would not all
be eaten before they had a chance to start growing. So, in place
of a few seed stalks, the pines were given many cones that were
tough and hard to break open. The pine cone develops as a
small embryo the first year on the new growth. Pollen is also
produced in great quantities on the same trees and carried by
the wind to fertilize these newly developed cones. By the end
of the summer they are hard and woody and ready to withstand

the coming winter. The second summer, the cones continue to grow larger and larger. When the seeds are ripe, the cone opens and out they come, ready to sprout the third year. But something new has also been added! The seeds are equipped with a little wing so the wind will carry them further than the cycad seeds that just fall to the ground. Quite an invention. But this is just the beginning. More modern plants have developed other ingenious ways of spreading their seeds. Some maple seeds are equipped with a double wing. Plants like the milkweed, cottonwood trees, dandelion and others have a little parachute arrangement that carries them much farther. Then when the air becomes cool and moist, the parachute closes and the seed falls to the ground. If the conditions where it lands are not just right, and turn out to be too dry, the parachute will open again, and away goes the seed in the wind to try some other location. The touch-me-not and a number of other plants produce their seeds in a pod that builds up a spring tension as the sections of the pod dry out. Finally it bursts open—shooting the seed ten to fifteen feet, or farther with the aid of the wind. As animals appeared on the earth, some seeds were given barbs, that catch in the fur and get a free ride. The tumbleweed grows like a ball and sprinkles its seeds across the country-side as it breaks loose and is blown along by the wind. Later forms of seed were produced in fruit—but nature also put an acid in this fruit to make it sour and give anyone a stomach ache who ate it too soon. But this acid turns to sugar when the seeds are ripe, and the fruit is offered as a tasty meal to anyone who will help carry the seeds to some new location. Some seaweeds put their seeds in little boats that float away but dissolve in two or three days, dropping the seed to the bottom. The wild oat, though, is more energetic and self-sufficient. Its seeds were given legs that are activated by changes in temperature and humidity, and these seeds start out walking on their own as can be seen through fast-motion photography, until they lodge in some place where they can start growing.

Along with all these improved methods of distributing seeds came improvements in the design of the seed itself. More modern seeds are placed in a regular seed container such as the pods of peas, beans, various types of nuts, berries, and fruits, all of which are the result of encasing seeds within the intricate parts of the newly created flowers. Here again was something entirely new—flowers of all shapes and sizes. Again nature was generous with color. There were white flowers, red flowers, yellow and black flowers. The first very simple flowers were pollinated by the wind, and even today these same varieties of plants are still dependent on the wind to carry their pollen from one flower to another. As new forms and shapes of insects appeared on the earth, nature added colorful petals, perfume and sweet nectar to the flowers of the more modern plants. But nature did not put color, perfume and nectar into the flowers to attract insects without a very definite purpose, and this was to use the insects to carry pollen from one flower to another.

The consistent progress and improvements in both the design and function of more modern plants, the many similarities between plants and animals and their increasing interdependence on each other became more and more overwhelming with each picture I made. It was also becoming increasingly apparent that some of these pictures of plants and flowers might reveal information of some considerable importance regarding both animals and human beings. The more pictures I took of plants and flowers, the more interested I became in them, and as I became more interested in them, the more pictures I continued to take.

Chapter 4

Project Sixty-One

As various industrial companies requested more time-lapse pictures, I had additional opportunities to photograph a still wider range of subjects. One film on the story of hybrid corn was of particular interest. Part of it showed pictures taken through a microscope of the germination of the grains of pollen on the corn silk. It further illustrated how each of the silks at the end of an ear of corn is attached to a kernel on the cob. At least one grain of pollen must fall from the anthers in the tassel at the top of the stalk on to each silk which is the stigma of the corn flower. The contents of the grain of dormant pollen then become active and commence moving about as the result of what appears to be some sort of a chemical stimulus received from the stigma. However, this movement is so slow that it becomes noticeable only when greatly speeded up through time-lapse photography. A tube grows from the microscopic grain of pollen and penetrates the full length of the corn silk, which

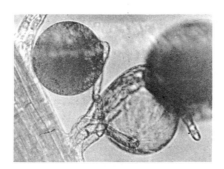

Pollen tube extending from pollen grain and penetrating hair of corn silk. Part of corn silk is shown at lower left.

may be twelve or fourteen inches long. The grain of pollen then discharges its contents which flow this entire distance. This illustrates how potent a single grain of pollen is, certainly something not to be trifled with.

When one or more kernels on a cob fail to develop properly, this may be due to pollen not having fallen on the silk leading to those particular kernels, or the silk may have been cut or damaged by an insect. It may also be due to bad weather conditions or a nutritional deficiency. When pollen from the same variety of corn falls on the silk, it produces an inbred variety; but pollen from another variety produces a hybrid. When two hybrids are crossed, the result is a double hybrid. Hybrids will not reproduce their own variety from seed, and these crosses must be made every year by seedsmen to produce seed for each crop of hybrid corn.

Different pollen respond in different ways to different stimulants. In some cases pollen would respond to merely being placed in contact with a piece of the stigma of its own flower, as might be expected would always be the case. The fact that the stigmas had been cut from the flowers may have been partially responsible for their not always readily activating the pollen. In some cases pollen germination resulted only after various mild chemicals were added, such as some of the amino acids, vitamins, hormones, yeast extracts or different combinations of these, along with the stigma of the right flower. In other cases the slides were mildly heated over an alcohol flame, and in one case results were not obtained until another pollen was also introduced along with the pollen being photographed. To begin with, the purpose of these pictures was in connection with advertising or public relations programs. Accordingly my primary purpose was merely to get the required picture. Time nor budget did not permit the keeping of complete records of just what was done in each instance; but this experience nevertheless was invaluable.

Meanwhile I had learned from several doctor friends that the irritation of the nasal membranes causing hay-fever was generally thought to result from simple contact with the outer surfaces of the grain of pollen in a way similar to that in which ordinary pepper causes people to sneeze. Apparently little consideration had been given to whether or not the pollen remained in a completely dormant state. Possibly the grains of pollen might be activated if the individual nasal fluids or body chemicals were just that which are necessary to activate the pollen in the same way the stigma of a flower does. These time-lapse pictures were the first that ever showed the primary stage of activity within a grain of pollen. As a result I learned a lot about pollen habits and reactions of many plants that had a commercial value, but, unfortunately, none of my clients was interested in transporting, canning, or otherwise growing or processing ragweed, so there was no opportunity of doing any work along these lines on a sponsored or paid basis.

From what little I had learned as a layman about hay-fever, these new observations on the reactions of corn pollen seemed quite exciting. Perhaps they might reveal some worthwhile information regarding ragweed pollen and how it causes hay-fever with some people and not others. As quickly as possible I made arrangements through a friend in the pharmaceutical business to meet one of the top authorities on pollen in the country. I showed him my time-lapse pictures taken through the microscope of the contents of a grain of corn pollen becoming active when it received the proper stimulus from the corn silk. At normal speed these reactions could not be noticed at all. The time-lapse pictures made it possible to see just when growth activities started and stopped, and when they speeded up or slowed down. They also clearly showed how certain activities going on within the stigma of a flower affect the grain of pollen when they come in contact with each other. The use of time-lapse photography, coupled with a microscope, made these growth activities apparent for the first time.

"Impossible," muttered the high authority in the country as I attempted to apply to ragweed pollen and hay-fever what my recently completed pictures on the story of hybrid corn showed regarding the germination of corn pollen. Had I realized how contrary to the accepted medical theory this reasoning was, I probably would have "tread" more lightly.

"Ridiculous," grumbled the top expert on such matters as he explained he had every book of any importance ever written on this subject in his library. There were sixty in all which un-

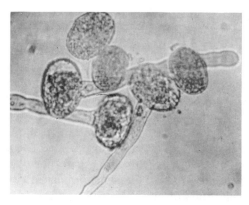

Partially developed pollen tubes growing from grains
of apple pollen. Contents in grains of pollen are
very active at this stage of development as seen
through time-lapse photography.

doubtedly included several written by himself. No mention was
made, either directly or by implication, in any of them that
could possibly substantiate my theory in the slightest. Furthermore, he pointed out it was obvious from my own pictures it
required at least an hour for a grain of pollen to develop a
pollen tube and discharge its contents. This did not tie into the
fact that anybody subject to hay-fever became immediately affected when walking from an air-conditioned room into the outdoor air during the pollen season. In addition to this objection,
it is common practice for various pharmaceutical companies to
put ragweed and other pollen through "an ether bath" to de-fat
them, and thereby increase their lasting qualities. This ether
treatment would positively kill any life within the pollen as
readily as alcohol kills all kinds of germs and bacteria. Yet
people reacted just as quickly, and just as violently to ether
de-fatted pollen as they did to so called "live" or "active" pollen.

This was discouraging, but nevertheless the pictures were
pretty good; and for people interested in the story of hybrid
corn, they created considerable favorable comment. As time
passed I made other films that required scenes of various different kinds of pollen germinating. Then one day something
happened that made me decide to devote as much time as possible to the further study of ragweed pollen, even though it

would have to be done on a sustaining basis. On this day nothing of particular interest had been happening. I did not bother to seal every slide to make it completely air tight. Suddenly I noticed some activity or change taking place in one of the slides, but could not be sure. It was like wondering if you really have a bite, or are just touching bottom when fishing. Unfortunately, the unsealed slides were already beginning to dry up. As a last resort I added a drop of plain distilled water to prolong the life of this particular subject to see if pollen tubes might eventually grow. They didn't because as soon as the distilled water was added, the grains of pollen began bursting from the capillary pressure of the increased moisture.

Wait a minute, my mind said: Could this have any significance with respect to a person subject to hay-fever walking from an air-conditioned room into the outdoor air during the pollen or hay-fever season? Maybe the moisture of the nasal passage would burst the grains of ragweed pollen and release the active contents without having to go through the step of first growing a pollen tube.

This certainly should be something of major interest to my friend with the sixty books, but he was totally unimpressed. The matter of the ether de-fatted pollen was still absolute proof against my completely unorthodox ideas. In spite of this, the chief obstacles had now been cut in half. I decided to throw budgets to the wind and go all out on another one of my sustaining projects during the following ragweed season.

During the spring and early summer I cultivated a good supply of both regular and giant ragweed. All summer the ragweed was carefully watered, fertilized and weeded. Some plants were brought into the time-lapse studio at different stages of growth for photographic observation. To do this, it was necessary to throw out other subjects before they were completed, subjects that had a commercial value. This almost broke my heart, but I had made up my mind to devote the basement time-lapse studio to nothing but ragweed, and so nothing but ragweed it was soon to be. Out went everything to make more and more room for additional tubs and pots of carefully cultivated ragweed.

Out went everything from the basement time-lapse studio to make room for carefully culti-vated ragweed. Twenty-four time-lapse cameras record growth reactions from every angle including microscopic pictures of ragweed pollen.

Additional plants were brought into the studio at various stages of development in order to have complete coverage with distant or wide-angle, medium close-up, extreme close-up and microscopic shots and at different angles. Probably no ragweed had ever been so completely photographed from all angles before. Soon the anthers developed in the spike-like staminate flowers that stand erect like the tassels on corn plants. Also the pistillate seed-producing flowers appeared at the leaf nodes, similar to the ears of corn. All the cameras were going steadily, day and night, some at five-minute intervals, some at two, ten and fifteen, to be certain of covering any possible unusual development.

The pollen season comes and goes within just a week or so with any particular group of plants of the same variety in a given locality. Therefore some space in the main time-lapse greenhouse was devoted to raising additional ragweed plants and delaying the pollen season by controlling the daylight periods in the same way that chrysanthemums are brought into bloom out of season.

The wide-angle, medium close-up and extreme close-up pictures were interesting and recorded the complete story on film of how ragweed grows, but the real exciting pictures were those taken through the microscopes. However, at first even these were disappointing for as hard as I tried to activate a grain of ragweed pollen so it would produce a pollen tube, it remained dormant.

Then I decided to follow another avenue of approach and obtained a sample of nasal secretion from a friend who suffered severely from hay-fever. Some ragweed pollen was placed in it, and put under one of the microscopes with a time-lapse camera. In watching this periodically through a special eye-piece, it seemed that little droplets of fluid were being given off through the many pores of the grains of pollen. This was something different from all the other·pollen I had previously worked with.

After about twenty-four hours and not waiting to finish the film, I pulled it from the camera and rushed it for processing. Finally the film came back, and the pictures clearly and unmistakably showed little droplets of fluid coming from the ragweed pollen. I immediately obtained more samples of nasal fluid from other friends who suffered from hay-fever, and kept one microscope and camera going continuously. In the other microscope I placed similar slides, except the ragweed pollen was in samples of nasal fluid obtained from people not subject to hay-fever.

In all I made approximately twelve such experiments, half hay-fever and half non hay-fever samples, and in each specimen from a person subject to hay-fever, the ragweed pollen gave off the droplets of fluid, and in each specimen from a person not subject to hay-fever the results were completely negative—no droplets given off. The ragweed pollen was from exactly the same source of supply in each instance.

Now the big question was: What would the ether de-fatted or dead pollen do under the same circumstances? I obtained some from my friend with the sixty books and set up the same series of experiments. It seemed to take forever, and it seemed like the time would never pass. Projects that in the past took several years to complete seemed like nothing. Twenty-four hours to take the pictures and another twenty-four hours to rush the film through processing seemed forever, but at last the film was ready for viewing through the projector. The first part showed negative results from the experiment made with nasal fluid from the person not subject to hay-fever.

Now the other part: The ether de-fatted dead pollen in the nasal fluid of a person suffering with hay-fever. I could hardly believe my eyes as the little droplets of fluid began to appear just as they did with fresh live pollen. This to me was one of the most exciting pictures I have ever taken. Of course, one test is not enough but more experiments revealed exactly the same results.

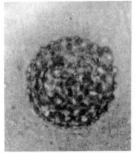 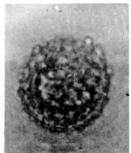 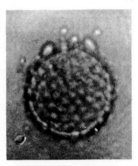

Ragweed pollen in nasal secretion of hay fever sufferer starts emitting tiny drops of liquid.

What does this mean? It is hard to say definitely, but I am hopeful that it may show that the body chemistry of people who suffer from hay-fever is just right to cause ragweed pollen to give off these little droplets of fluid, which in turn might possibly be the irritating factor to the nasal membranes rather than the mere contact with the outer surface of the dormant grains of pollen themselves. If this is so, then the exact chemical balance of the particular individual that causes this activity might be altered by raising or lowering such things as the sugar ratio or acidity (P.H.) or something else vital to ragweed pollen. Possibly hay-fever could then be prevented rather than trying to cure it or counteract it with medicines after the irritation has once set in.

The fact that the ragweed pollen, in giving off these little droplets of fluid, reacted differently from all the other pollens I had worked with was noteworthy. Was this another exception to the laws of nature pertaining to the habits of pollen, or had I just not yet hit on the right combination of things to activate the contents so a pollen tube would start growing? The season was just about at an end, even including the plants which I had delayed in the greenhouse. I tried one last experiment to activate the contents of ragweed pollen by using both a part of the stigma of the ragweed flower together with nasal fluid from a person subject to hay-fever. There was a short end of film left in one camera and no more film on the shelf at the time. When it came back from processing, it showed activity in one grain of ragweed pollen and starting in a second. The film ran out before a pollen tube started to develop, but I now feel reasonably certain a tube would grow in the normal course of events. That was the last of that year's ragweed, and there was nothing more that could be done until the following year when the ragweed would bloom again.

Chapter 5

Growth Responses to Variations in Temperature

One film on tuberculosis for Eastman Kodak Company caused much difficulty and convinced me that some subjects looked more simple than they really were. The project was designed to demonstrate the use of X-ray films in diagnosing the disease, and it seemed to me that it would be interesting to illustrate a spot of TB on the lung by comparing it to a black spot on a rose leaf.

Dr. Earl Barth, Head of the Department of Radiology (X-ray) at Northwestern University Medical School, collaborated with the production and actually took part in it. Dr. Barth explained in a popular way that plants breathe through their leaves and animals breathe through their lungs. Consequently for purposes of illustration there was some interest in comparing a black spot on a rose leaf and a spot of TB on a lung. They are both serious if not quickly eradicated. One obvious difference, however, is that a black spot on a rose leaf is easily visible, but in order to detect a spot of TB on a lung, an X-ray picture or radiograph is required.

To illustrate this difference graphically, it was decided to show microscopic time-lapse pictures of the growth of the spores of the black spot organism. Dr. O. J. Eigsti, who had helped with microscopic pictures of pollen, obtained a pure strain of spores of *Diplocarpon rosae*, and we set out to take pictures of their growth.

This is the type of picture on which it is almost impossible to estimate a budget in advance because unexpected problems may arise. Both Dr. Eigsti and I could think of no reason why we couldn't complete this picture in one day. Maybe cameras might have to run during the night to obtain good growth of the fungus, but beyond this there should be nothing to it.

A batch of microscopic slides were made up on the morning the project was started. We used our previously proven method of an agar base sealed under a cover-slip to prevent drying out. Two time-lapse microscopic cameras were started, and we figured the growth activity should be evident by lunch time or shortly after.

By late afternoon no fungus growth was yet evident, nor late that night, nor even the next morning. The same procedure was repeated the following day. Again no luck, so at this point the budget had to be set aside again, and further experiments charged up to experience. Here was another challenge to see why the spores wouldn't grow, as it was so hard to keep them from growing on the roses outdoors in the garden.

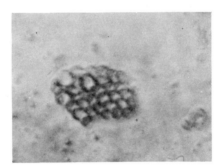

Black spot spores in dormant condition.

We tried using rose leaves in place of the agar, combinations of rose leaves, agar and growth stimulants previously used in connection with the pollen tube pictures, but nothing happened. We decided the trouble must be that the cultures were dead, but we had no better luck with additional new cultures. We tried all sorts of ways of making our own fresh culture taken directly from rose leaves with black spot. Days turned into weeks, months, and not the slightest encouragement. I brought rose plants into my time-lapse studio and tried all sorts of ways of

transmitting black spot to the leaves. I scratched them with a
needle and rubbed these leaves with infected leaves. I rubbed
spores on the top of leaves and underneath, on the stems and
roots. Different varieties of roses were tried, but still nothing
happened. I pricked them and broke them and tore them in
half, but the rose plants in the time-lapse studio remained
perfectly healthy. This was hard to understand, as the preven-
tion of black spot was always a major problem with both ama-
teur and commercial growers of roses, whether grown indoors
or out.

The situation was no longer funny. No usable pictures yet,
and the final deadline for the completion of the film already
extended, time running out again, and oh, the budget! Still I
wanted to follow this through further, even if just for my own
satisfaction and experience. Dr. Eigsti had other commitments
coming up that would make it impossible for him to continue
longer. He felt everything possible had been tried but to no
avail, so it was decided this project would have to be given up,
at least for the present. Nevertheless, I asked him to make one
last batch of twelve more slides to leave with me, and I would
keep on trying as long as they lasted. This he did, and then
departed. We were both pretty sad about our complete failure.

After he left I put one slide in each of the two microscopes
and started the cameras going. It seemed almost useless, as
there was nothing any different from what we had been doing
for months, but maybe the spores might start to grow this time.
As soon as everything was in order and running smoothly, I
looked down at the remaining ten slides that Dr. Eigsti had
left, and wondered if I might have picked the right two slides
to begin with. If any of them were going to germinate, they
would probably start at the same time like a row of seeds in the
garden. Would it be just my luck to have several of the ten
slides germinate at once, and neither of the two in the microscope being photographed? Maybe germination of the ten could
be delayed by putting them in the kitchen refrigerator until
those in the microscopes could be tested for a sufficient period
of time.

The next morning the two slides in the microscopes showed
absolutely no sign of any fungus growth having taken place. I

felt a little foolish to have ever held out the slightest hope that
things might have been any different this time.

Now, what about those ten slides in the refrigerator? I hated
to think of all the good film already wasted. This was really
going too far, but strange things had happened before, and the
microscopes and cameras had been scheduled for these ten more
slides. Out went the first two slides, and two more from the
kitchen refrigerator went into their places. Before there was
even time to start the cameras, the spores looked different.
Something was happening. I quickly started both cameras and
watched intently. Within an hour something different was happening. The threadlike fungus growth was definitely showing.
Each day for four more days, two additional slides were brought
down from the refrigerator, and all of them germinated and
grew perfectly. When the film was projected, the protoplasmic
contents or cytoplasm of the spores showed a characteristic
activity before any threadlike fungus growth started. This
activity was quite similar to what showed within the grains of
pollen before a pollen tube would grow.

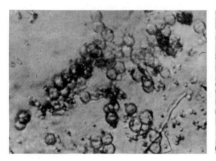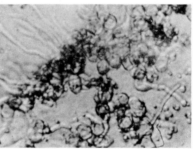

The contents or cytoplasm of spores that cause black spot on rose leaves appeared active through time-lapse photography after chilling overnight in kitchen refrigerator.

Threadlike fungus growth readily develops after cytoplasm of spores has been activated.

It was a great relief to finally have the time-lapse pictures
of the spore growth in the nick of time for use in the film on
X-rays. It was even more of a personal satisfaction to have
gotten them at all after so many months. There seemed to be
some justification for having gone completely overboard as far

as the budget was concerned. I shuddered though with the thought of what would have to be charged up to experience.

Now the question: What was it about the kitchen refrigerator that made these spores grow when they had been put there to hold them back? It so happened that I was also making a film at the same time on spring flowers. I had just finished studying the necessary cooling period spring bulbs must have before they will start growing. The same chilling process seemed to apply to the spores that cause black spots on rose leaves. At least this seemed to be a plausible answer to what had happened with respect to the spore cultures suddenly growing on the slides that had been chilled.

But what about the fact that the black spot disease could not be induced to grow on any of the rose plants in my time-lapse studio? In checking back on this, the night temperature control of the day-and-night double-acting thermostat was found not to be working properly. The same even temperature was accidentally being maintained both day and night in the studio. When this was corrected, and the night temperature lowered considerably, it was no trick at all to develop black spot on the leaves of the rose plants in the time-lapse studio.

This might possibly open up some new ideas for further research in the control of black spot and other similar plant diseases by commercial growers of greenhouse roses. However, there are also important factors to consider regarding the most desirable day and night temperatures necessary from the point of view of obtaining the best roses; that is—size of flower, length of stem, sturdiness, color and other qualities that must be considered.

Several years later the importance of the variation of day and night temperatures with light and darkness again became apparent. An advertising agency wanted a time-lapse picture of a rose opening in order to present their client's new product on television. Ordinarily, the petals of a rose open part way the first day and then close up somewhat during the night period. Each successive day the petals open a little wider and again fold together at night. This closing action at night was troublesome, and the advertising agency wanted the rose to open with a steady continuous motion. To try and accomplish this, the rose was placed under continuous artificial light indoors where it would not receive any sunlight. The temperature control was set to maintain an even constant temperature during both the day and night periods. It was hoped that the even temperature and continuous light would make the rose bud grow steadily without the closing action during the normal night period. It was found the rose would do this for approximately forty-eight hours, but then the petals would collapse as though overcome with exhaustion even though the bud was only half-way open. Ordinarily a fairly well developed rose bud will develop to full maturity even when cut and placed in water. Apparently though even a cut flower must have its regular night's sleep, and enjoys or responds more favorably to lower temperatures during this period. To accomplish this picture, it was necessary to start with a rose bud more nearly open and photograph it

Check plants being grown outdoors for comparison with results obtained on similar plants in time-lapse greenhouse.

under the continuous light and even temperature for only approximately forty-eight hours.

The growth of most plants takes place only during the daylight hours, and they seem to relax or literally go to sleep during the dark night period. Corn, however, continues to grow during both the day and night hours although the growth that takes place during the night is noticeably yellowish in color. This turns green during the daytime. The growth that takes place during the daylight hours is green right from the start. An interesting comparison of the growth response during the day and night hours can be made with fish. Certain tropical fish will grow faster and mature much quicker if kept under continuous artificial light for twenty-four hours a day. It is thought these fish actually sleep part of the time even though they have no eyelids and cannot shut out the light from their eyes.

There is one more point to mention here regarding the microscopes, particularly for anyone more interested in the technical aspects of this matter of temperature. They are both enclosed together with the cameras and other related equipment in an incubator cabinet with absolute temperature control. It must be accurate within plus or minus two-tenths of a degree, as any greater variation of temperature will throw the high-powered lenses out of focus as the changes in temperature expand and contract the metal in the microscope.

With the film on X-rays completed, I thought this matter of chilling the spores was closed, but it soon was evident that perhaps it actually was just beginning. At this time I caught a common head cold. Perhaps it was from getting chilled while working one evening in the time-lapse studio with the black spot experiment. I began thinking more about this matter of chilling. I read what there was on the subject in several encyclopedias and asked two or three doctor friends. The present theories are pretty indefinite and uncertain except in regard to chilling. Here it is fairly well agreed that chilling lowers the resistance of the body tissues, making an individual more susceptible to the attacking organisms, which are thought, but not proven, to be some sort of a virus. Could it be possible that instead of lowering the resistance of the body tissue, that chilling might stimulate or activate the attacking organisms, whatever they might be. This would be the same principle or law of nature as the chilling that activated the black spot spores, spring bulbs and many plants and trees. If so, then this might explain conflicting reports from reliable sources regarding whether or not actual chilling of the body is in any way connected with catching cold. Chilling would result in catching cold only if the cold-causing organisms were present in the body at the time of chilling. Furthermore these cold-causing agents might be present in the body in an inactive or dormant condition for some period of time, and then be activated as the result of chilling. The amount of chilling necessary of course could be an important factor. Some spring bulbs need only thirty days at fifty degrees Fahrenheit. The spores worked fine being placed in the kitchen refrigerator over night, but perhaps ten minutes or less might have done the trick. Possibly the temperature might not have needed to be anywhere as cool or cold as it happened to be at the time, which I estimated was approximately forty-five degrees Fahrenheit. The matter of normal temperature of the human body is in itself fascinating indeed, for only one half of one degree over normal is considered to be somewhat of a fever.

The more I thought about this matter of chilling, the more far-reaching the possible application seemed to be. I decided to take some time-lapse microscopic pictures of my own nasal secretion at the time I had that bad head cold, just to see what might show up in the pictures. Any sort of virus would be too small to show, but maybe some reactions might be noticeable, so I started subjects in both microscopes one evening. The next morning both showed a well-developed threadlike fungus growth. When the films were processed and could be projected on the screen, the actual growth development of this fungus was clearly visible, together with formation of new spore-heads.

This was something quite exciting, but of course there were many ways that some spores could have found their way onto that slide. There are all kinds of them just floating in the air. I waited until over the cold and repeated the same experiment. No fungus growth appeared at all in twelve samples taken under the same conditions over a two-weeks' period. Exactly the same positive and negative results were obtained with similar tests made with samples taken from four other persons who had head colds, and again after they were completely recovered. In each instance the same characteristic type of fungus growth and spore-head was in evidence. It was even more interesting to me that with three persons who had a deep chest cold and laryngitis that an entirely different type of spore and fungus growth was evident. Again samples taken from the same people at a later date, when they were over their deep chest colds and laryngitis, showed negative results.

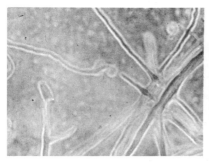 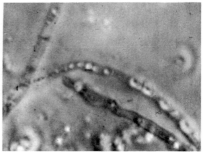

Fungus growth found in nasal secretion during early stages of ordinary
head cold.

Fungus growth found in nasal secretion during early stages of deep chest
cold and laryngitis.

Both types of fungus would grow rapidly in the thin watery nasal fluid obtained during the early stages of a cold, but with the thickened discharge taken during the advanced stages of a cold, the reaction was quite different. Microscopic time-lapse pictures show that nasal discharge is thickened as a result of the presence of multitudes of some sort of cell that is in a constant state of activity, but again, activity only noticeable when greatly speeded up through time-lapse photography. In those areas where active cells were present, the fungus would not grow, but would grow all around those areas where the active cells were not present.

The close similarity between the symptoms of hay-fever and an ordinary head cold make it very hard sometimes to definitely differentiate between them. Likewise the similar characteristics of not only the appearance but also the growth habits of

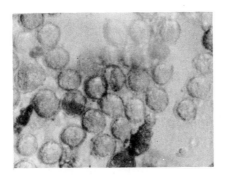

These cells appear in nasal discharge as cold progresses and appear extremely active through time-lapse photography. No activity is noticeable at normal speed.

spores and pollen are such that it is frequently difficult to tell one from the other. The activity of the contents is very similar, and in many instances the threadlike fungus growth of spores resembles so closely the tubes developing from pollen grains.

Prior to the introduction of the new Salk vaccine, both my wife and I were always a little concerned during the polio season whenever any of the children showed symptoms of a grippy type of cold. The early symptoms of polio are very similar to a cold and hay-fever. We have always been advised not to let our children get chilled or overly tired, for it does seem to be recognized that polio is associated with chilling from swimming in cold water or other sudden similar cooling effects. Polio is seasonal and comes during the end of the summer period, which is recognized also as the height of the mold season in regard to hay-fever sufferers. The growth period of certain spores could be as seasonal as the blooming period of the flowering plants with which everybody is much more familiar. This is certainly worth taking note of.

Following one talk I gave with my pictures, a chemist told me he had found that the incidence of certain types of food poisoning rose rapidly with the practice of re-heating food after it had been refrigerated. Possibly certain air-borne bacteria and spores that settle on the food become activated again as the result of refrigeration. When these foods are removed from the refrigerator, it is like going from mid-winter into the warm spring temperatures that makes everything start to grow again.

During the production of a film for a large paper company, I learned from one of their research people that the paper industry is often faced with the problem of a bacterial or mold growth developing every now and then in the wet wood pulp that is rolled into continuous sheets of paper. This can cause considerable loss of time and production in addition to the cost of cleaning the equipment. There are also other industries that either actually use certain mold growths or have problems controlling it that might be affected by various growth reactions as stimulated by changes of temperature.

Another time-lapse project worth commenting on in regards to temperature change was designed to show the difference in growth of plants when given a complete balanced plant food. This picture was to show two similar tomato plants growing side by side. They were both in the same poor soil, but one had been fed the particular plant food to be illustrated. Final approval to start the project was not received until hot summer had already arrived. There were also considerable delays with the installation of some new ventilating equipment for the time-lapse studio. To my surprise, there was no noticeable difference in the growth between the two plants being photographed or additional check plants that I had also growing in the greenhouse. This experiment was started over again several times, but it was not until fall when the weather and temperature in my greenhouse was considerably cooler that a noticeable difference between the fed and unfed plants was evident. Then the difference was so great that it was almost unbelievable. Again variations in temperature during the day and night period are an important factor in not only directly stimulating growth of the plants but also in stimulating soil bacteria. These in turn help break down the minerals in the plant food and make them available in a form that can be taken up by the roots of plants. This is a subject that holds tremendous possibilities for further study.

The gardenia is a particularly good example of a plant that is very sensitive to variations in day and night temperatures. The flower buds can stand quite warm temperature during the daytime providing there is sufficient sunlight. However, if the night temperature is not maintained below 65 degrees Fahrenheit, the flower buds will turn yellow and drop off. All the growth energy of the plant is then directed toward producing new leaf growth. The relationship between light intensity and temperature is an important factor in many other plants also. Just as some plants are forced into bloom ahead of the normal season by controlling the light and dark periods, the azalea can be forced into bloom ahead of time by controlling temperature. It is a common practice now for commercial growers of this plant to force early bloom by placing the plants in cold storage refrigerators and advancing the normal winter season. When the temperature is maintained at 40 degrees Fahrenheit, the plants may be kept in total darkness for twenty-four hours a day for several weeks without the plants losing their leaves. Above this temperature the azalea plants will lose their leaves unless there is an increasing amount of light as the temperature is raised above the 40 degree mark. After the plants have had the necessary winter chilling, they can then be forced into bloom in a warm greenhouse during the regular winter months.

From other information gained as a result of having produced a film on the story of garden pests and insects for Swift and Company, I am convinced that some insects must be chilled before they will complete the pupa stage. The cocoon or chrysalis is not solely for the purpose of self-preservation during the winter period. It is known that many moths and butterflies will not emerge from cocoon or chrysalis if brought into the house too early in the fall. It is thought the reason is that they dry out if kept inside too long. There is little if any information regarding the necessity of chilling in connection with insects, but there is considerable information available as to just how much warm weather is required for certain insects to emerge from the pupa stage. In discussing this with several just plain good old-fashioned nature-study teachers—if I may refer to them as such—I am told that if cocoons are placed in the refrigerator for awhile, when brought indoors early in the fall, that then there is no problem about their drying out. The butterflies and moths will emerge perfectly.

One day I noticed a picture on the back page of a Chicago paper of two penguins. One was a king penguin and the other a fairy penguin. The caption mentioning that the small fairy penguin was a species, that never normally grew very large; and that penguins very rarely, or virtually never, reproduce any young in captivity. This made me curious, so I asked the director of one of the large zoos what animals most rarely reproduced any young in captivity, and what the theory was about this. He quickly named several animals—reindeer, polar bears, penguins—and with a few exceptions those animals ordinarily found at the Arctic or Antarctic regions. He further explained that the generally accepted theory about this was that these animals were the farthest removed from civilization, and therefore the psychological impact was greatest on them when brought into captivity and caged up in a zoo.

Maybe the fur of these animals might be so thick that they are too warm in our climate. It has been medically proven that the human male reproductive organs must remain slightly cooler than the body itself or otherwise may become sterile. This resulting slight variation in temperature is the most important reason for correcting an undescended testicle.

Although the penguin cages in some zoos are air-conditioned during the summer months, they are never the equivalent of real Arctic or Antarctic weather. Although I am certainly not an authority on this subject, and have no books in my library that mention anything about it, I doubt that the psychological impact of being caged up should be so much greater on a polar bear than on any other kind of bears that nature's laws of instinct would not overcome. Besides most zoos are closed to the eyeing public at night and the nights are just as dark in many zoos as they are in the great open spaces.

When I first thought about this whole story of comparing the chilling effect on black spot spores with spring bulbs, it seemed so simple and obvious that surely it must have been written in the records and long since forgotten, but maybe all the effects of chilling have not been fully recognized in the past.

Chapter 6

Hindsight

In thinking back over various time-lapse projects, there is one in particular that seems to tie in closely to the effects of chilling. Early in the summer of 1948 Northwestern University Medical School was interested in a project of time-lapse study of the growth and division of cancer cells. Information of a new type phase-contrast microscope had recently been released, but following the war deliveries of all such equipment were still very slow and uncertain. Northwestern University Medical School had one on order from the Bausch & Lomb Optical Company. They had been quoted a two-year delivery date. This seemed a long way off and was very disappointing. However, it so happened I gave a lecture and showed some of my time-lapse pictures in Rochester, New York, where the headquarters of the Bausch & Lomb Company are located. Following the lecture, as was usually the case, a number of people came down front to ask questions. This particular night I was pressed for time to catch a train on to my next speaking engagement and had possibly been a little hasty in trying to pack up all the projection equipment and be on my way. On the train while pulling ticket stubs and similar miscellaneous items out of my pockets, there was a card I remembered receiving from an elderly gentleman. He had made the casual remark about being interested in time-lapse pictures, and for me to be sure to let him know if he could ever be of any help. Lots of people had frequently made this same remark just as conversation, so I had not taken this particular gentleman too seriously at the time. However, upon looking at the card again, I noticed he happened to be president of the Bausch & Lomb Optical Company. Could he be really serious in wanting to help in any way possible? Immediately upon arriving home, a letter to him was in the mail. The result was Northwestern Medical School had a phase-contrast microscope within two weeks instead of the estimated two years.

This accomplished, the next step was to design and have made some special glass chambers that would fit within the restricted space of this new type microscope. They had to be optically perfect so as not to cause any refraction of light. The glass chamber held a regular cover-slip with the living cancer tissue suspended underneath. It was also equipped with an intake and discharge glass tube so a continuous flow of fresh plasma could be supplied to keep the cancer cells growing. Next an incubator cabinet was built with special access doors. Adjustments could be made on the microscope by reaching in through these small doors and not materially lowering the temperature of the entire cabinet. Finally a system of transporting the tissue culture slides in heated Thermos jugs from the medical school to the time-lapse studio was worked out so that the exact body temperature could be maintained while the slides were in transit. This was considered to be of the utmost importance, so that the subjects would not be chilled or otherwise subjected to any harmful effects.

The tissue culture slides were prepared from rat tumors. New slides were prepared every few days and brought out to the studio, a distance of approximatedy fifteen miles. This project continued all summer and well into the following winter. Dozens and dozens of slides were prepared and carefully transported in the heated Thermos jugs, but not a single picture showed any cell division taking place. Everybody had been so optimistic and hopeful that this project might reveal some important information through time-lapse photography. Unfortunately the results had so far been very disappointing, and the enthusiasm on the part of those participating was rapidly waning. Serious consideration was being given to the question of how much longer it was worthwhile to carry this project further. Then one day the intern who was bringing the heated Thermos jug carelessly allowed the cover to jiggle loose in the back of the car and come off. The slides were cold on arrival, and we both felt they obviously had been completely ruined. We came very close to throwing them out, but inasmuch as the cameras were all ready and nothing else was available to photograph at the moment, I put them in the microscopes anyway, and started the cameras going. There was just enough film on the end of a full magazine for one more time-lapse sequence. When the film was finished, it went in for processing as usual.

It had become rather monotonous, looking at film after film of these cancer cell pictures and nothing ever happening. As this particular film was projected, it seemed to be the same story over again. The first part showed no cell division. The last part of it contained the sequence of the cancer cells that had become cold and then reheated to body temperature. Would they look any different as the result of having been chilled? Finally this sequence was on the screen, and the cells did look different! They seemed more active, alive. Suddenly one pulled together into a compact round shape. The chromosomes within the cell lined up and split in two as the cancer cell actually divided. It was hard to realize that after all these months of

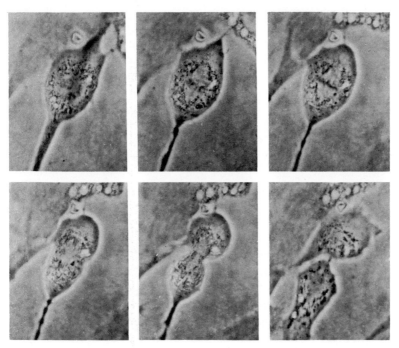

Time-lapse sequence showing division of cancer cell. Chromosomes can clearly be seen as they line up across center of cell and split in two as process of mitosis takes place.

work here was the picture we were after, and it had happened with a slide that through carelessness had been chilled so that we considered it hardly worth photographing at all. This was the first slide that showed any cell division. We didn't know why, but from then on discontinued transporting the slides in the heated Thermos jugs. I recorded in my notes that it just worked better that way, and put down a great big question mark. From then on we were able to get all the pictures of cell division we wanted, and the project was soon completed. The more recent observations on the effect of chilling certain bulbs and black spot spores seem to tie in with stimulating cell division in these earlier cancer pictures, but the question as to just what the significance might be needs further study.

Ordinarily warmth is associated with stimulating growth and cold retarding it. Still sitting in the warm sun on a hot day makes one lazy or sleepy, while cool weather or a quick dip in cold water is very invigorating. It is interesting how temperature controls certain growth responses of some plants more than others. The tulip grows exceedingly well in Holland where the prevailing winds off the North Sea both moderate the winters and make the summers cool. The temperature averages 35 degrees Fahrenheit during January and 66 in July. Tulip bulb production is limited to areas where the soil temperature remains below 50 degrees Fahrenheit for long periods of time. Higher temperatures of other localities ripen the bulb too quickly after flowering and do not allow enough time to store up energy and produce the next year's flower bud. This makes the bulb and resulting flower smaller each year in many areas where other flowers not so critically affected by temperature such as day-lilies, peonies, iris and many more, get larger after the first year and spread out to produce more flowers. The foliage of these other plants remains green after the flowers are finished blooming and adds beauty to a garden all summer long.

In addition to light and temperature, there are other influencing factors controlling plant growth such as humidity and possibly also changes in barometric pressure. Plants have a tendency to grow much smaller at higher altitudes. Many of the miniature alpine flowers found on mountain peaks belong to the same plant families as the much larger varieties that grow at lower altitudes. Many of the so-called oriental dwarf trees have merely been brought down from the higher mountain peaks and transplanted into fancy looking pots. The timberline, that is the altitude above which trees will not grow, is well over 20,000 feet at the equator. In the State of Colorado it averages 11,500 feet above sea level, and the further you go from the equator toward either the North or South Pole, the lower the timberline is. At the Arctic circle the timberline is right down to sea level, and further north there are no trees at all.

Another curious and unusual phenomenon that was revealed in the time-lapse pictures of cancer cells was the presence of some extremely active cells that put out pseudopods and quickly retracted them with an amoeboid type motion. These active cells only appeared in those tissue culture slides with cancer cells present. They did not appear in the normal tissue cultures. This of course could have been purely coincidental, but nevertheless was of some interest. The motion referred to was much faster in relation to any other normal cell activity. In fact, it was positively violent by comparison. No one has yet been able to positively identify these extremely active cells, which only become apparent through time-lapse photography.

In one of my most recent pictures of ragweed pollen in the nasal fluid of a person subject to hay-fever, a similar type of active cell is present. This time, however, it starts from a perfectly dormant cell and gradually becomes more active as the grains of ragweed pollen give off the little droplets of fluid. There is also a similarity of motion in the cells present in the thickened nasal fluid at the advanced stage of a head cold that seemed to control or prevent the penetration of the fungus growth. I believe these violently active cells have something to do with nature's way of combating disease or disorders in the chemical balance of the human body. Heretofore this activity has gone unnoticed because it could not be seen at normal speed, but now becomes apparent through time-lapse photography. These highly active cells seem to be influenced by chemical changes within the body fluids and may be of quite some importance in maintaining the normal balance of the body chemistry. I believe they are worthy of further serious study.

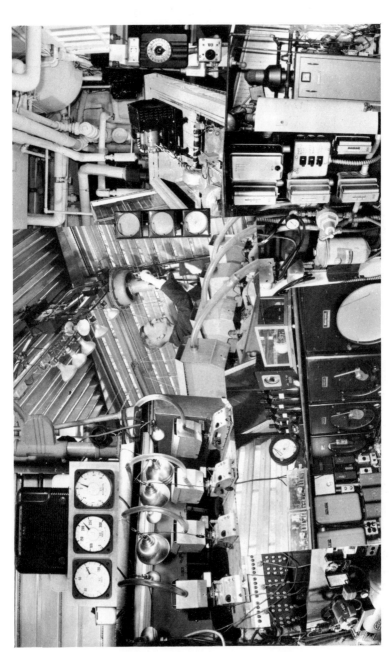

Time-lapse greenhouse control area. Dials in upper left indicate out-put voltage of special control transformers, voltage of current received from utility company and load in kilowatts being used. Left center—controlled artificial light growing area. Lower left—air compressor that operates large greenhouse shutters. Top center—adjustment being made on pneumatic diaphragm type motor that opens and closes large aluminum shutters. Cuckoo appears from clock each time picture is taken when bird control switch is on. Lower center —three rotating cams behind round circular glass panel doors control open position of greenhouse shutters so they automatically follow the position of the sun. In this way they permit the greatest amount of direct sunlight to enter. Upper right—water pipes, air ducts and electrical equipment. Center right—compressor for refrigeration temperature controlled growing area. Also timing device for controlling

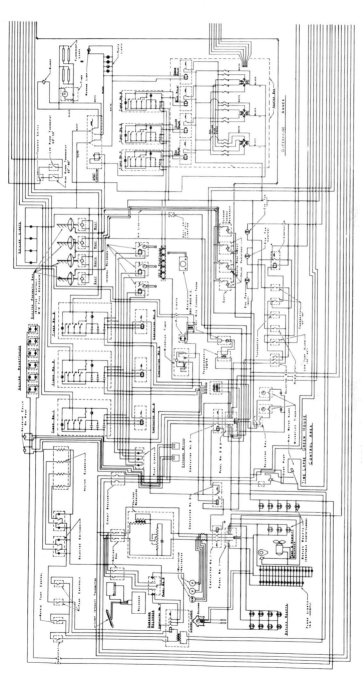

Wiring diagram, time-lapse greenhouse control area.

Young son, Henry assists in checking time-lapse cameras. Plastic hoses bring cool dehumidified air to aluminum hoods over each time-lapse camera. This provides proper temperature and humidity, making it possible to keep color film in cameras for long periods of time. Temperature is ordinarily maintained at 50° Fahrenheit and humidity approximately 45 per cent. Subjects being photographed top row left to right include oranges, bird of paradise flowers, azalea, banana plant and vanilla orchid. Bottom row left to right, cattleya orchids, gardenia, camellia, chocolate tree seedling and coffee tree, extreme lower right background.

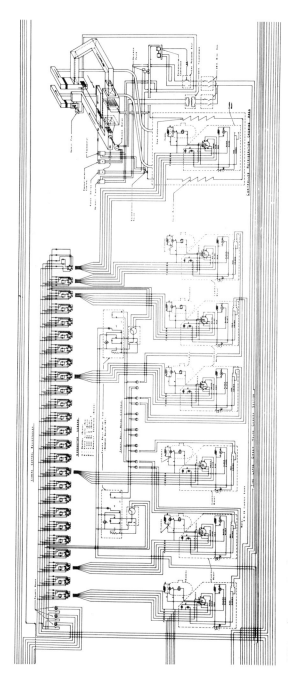

Wiring diagram, time-lapse greenhouse camera section, including controlled refrigeration growing area. Twenty-five camera plug-in receptacles are shown; however, only six cameras are included in drawing due to space limitations. Cameras may also be suspended from ceiling brackets.

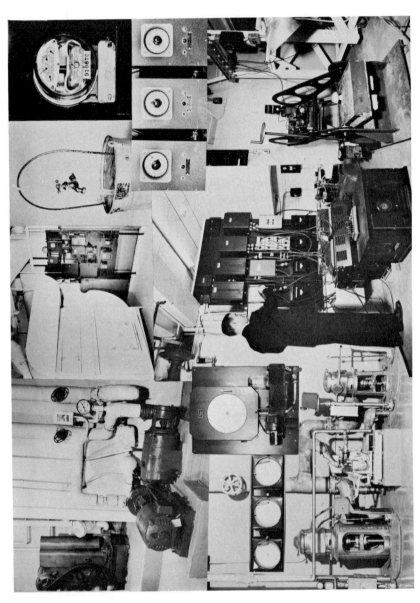

Central control area. Upper left to right: Deep well pump for air conditioning system and pressure pumps for disposing of water through lawn sprinkling system. Air conditioning plenum chamber and controls. Trick water faucet and electric meter. Bottom left to right: Two electric sump pumps and standby gasoline motor driven pump for emergency use. Time-lapse control equipment and special electric driven automatic tilt-down mechanism photographing growth of mushroom.

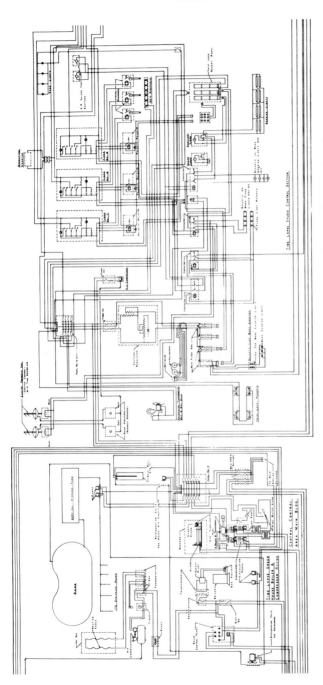

Wiring diagram, central control area in main building and also time-lapse studio control section.

Main time-lapse table in basement studio. Supplemental fluorescent growing lights can be seen suspended from above. Pattern of sunlight and shadows on far wall is from overhead skylight and automatic shutters. Fifteen time-lapse cameras are photographing various spring bulbs from all angles.

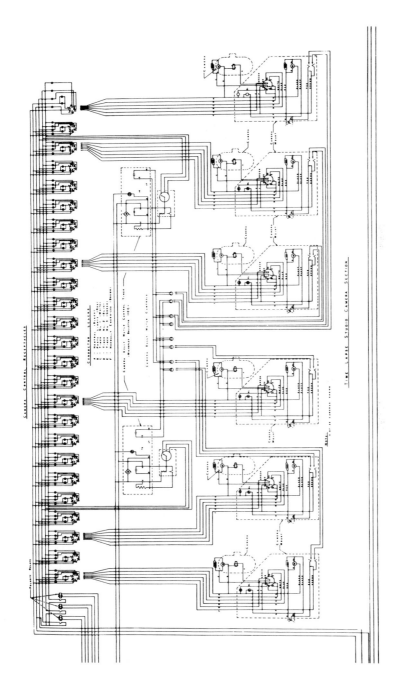

Wiring diagram, time-lapse studio, camera section. Again all twenty-five camera plug-in receptacles are indicated, but only six cameras shown due to space limitations of drawing.

Improved time-lapse microscopic unit contained in plastic incubator cabinet. Electric motors suspended underneath operate through gear reduction drive to move microscope stage very slowly in any direction. This makes it possible to follow a moving subject on the microscope slide and keep it in the field being photographed.

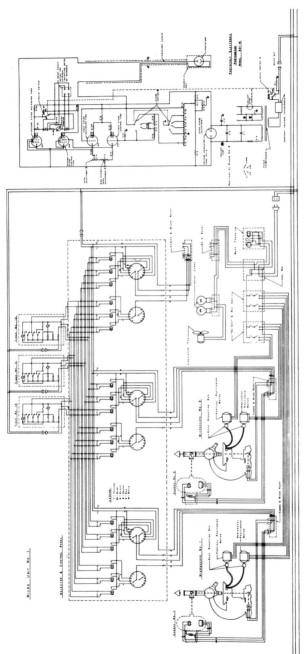

Wiring diagram, microscopic time-lapse unit.

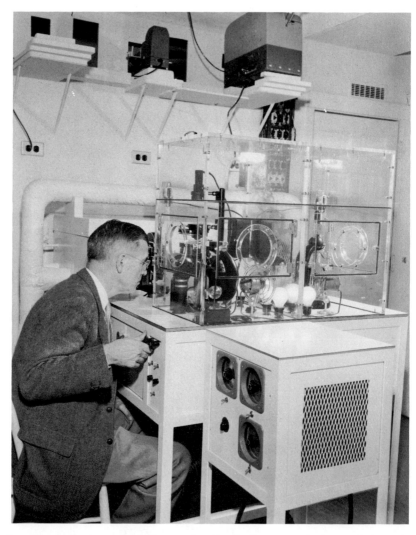

Latest improved microscopic time-lapse unit with all microscope controls extended outside of plastic cabinet. In background is special heating and refrigeration unit for controlling the temperature of the microscope stage and subject being photographed. Smaller cabinet in foreground contains all automatic timing equipment that might jar or move subject being photographed in microscope.

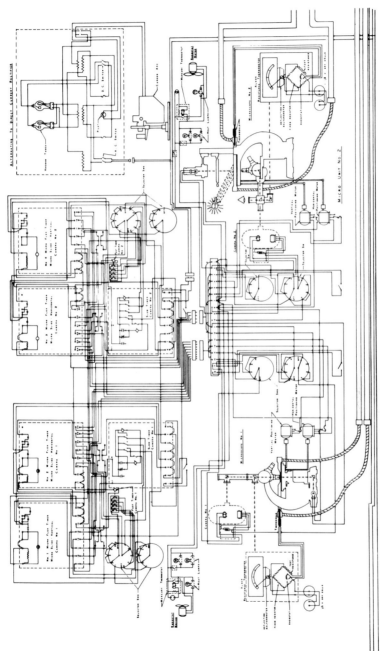

Wiring diagram of latest improved microscopic time-lapse unit.

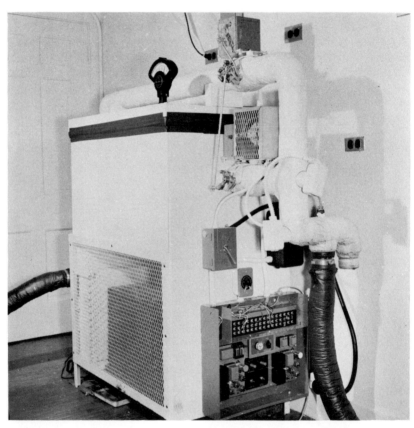

Specially designed heating and refrigeration unit to control temperature of microscope slide. Temperature range 0° to 250° Fahrenheit. Temperature electronically controlled within plus or minus ½°.

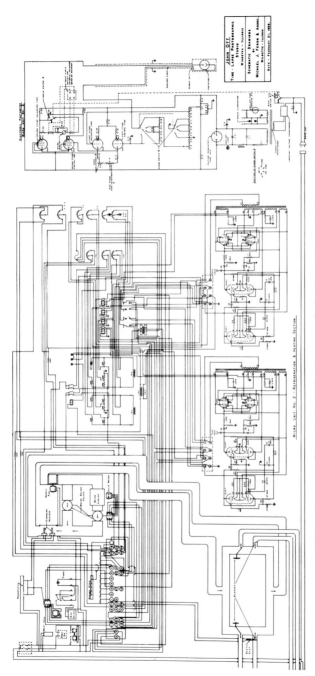

Wiring diagram, refrigeration and heating controls for latest improved microscopic time-lapse unit.

Chapter 7

Pink or Blue? The Effect of Wave Length of Light Energy on Growth Response in Plants

The waltzing flowers were not the only subjects that required special equipment. I had experienced considerable difficulty in trying to make time-lapse pictures of corn growing in the glass greenhouse. Although the pictures were good, the corn always grew spindly. The ears would not develop to normal size, and the leaves were long and narrow. It was not possible to take time-lapse pictures of corn growing outdoors because of the wind and weather. The leaves would be in a different position for each picture. Finally I tried growing corn outdoors and letting different plants develop to different stages. Then I built a make-shift enclosure around them and tried to photograph the formation of the ears and tassels after the plant had grown out in the open up to the time these parts began to appear. In making the enclosure, it was more convenient to use some of the new plastic sheeting that had just come on the market. The corn grew much more normally under plastic than it did under glass so I began experimenting with the growing of corn and other plants under different kinds of plastic. Most ordinary glass stops over 99 per cent of the ultraviolet radiation whereas some plastics allow approximately 95 per cent or more to pass through. The practice of old-time experienced nurserymen in completely removing the glass sash from the cold frames during the daytime to expose the young seedling plants to direct sunlight always interested me. The improved growth warranted the additional labor of completely removing the sash in place of raising it a little for ventilation during the daytime, and replacing it again at night when there might be danger of frost.

The results of using plastic in place of glass were so much better that I decided to build a new plastic greenhouse entirely without glass. This was unheard of at the time, so I had to call on my friend, Herman Schubert, again to fabricate the entire structure in his machine shop. It was built in sections, then dismantled and moved to the selected location in the back yard where it was reassembled again.

New all-plastic and aluminum time-lapse greenhouse. Double vestibule doors provide both light trap and wind break so that pictures are not spoiled if automatic timer should operate while door is open.

Compared with the skylight over the basement time-lapse studio, the new plastic greenhouse was a big improvement. The entire roof area as well as the east, south, and west sides were

At one time my wife thought I was spending too much time editing film in the basement so I moved upstairs, but not for very long.

made of clear plastic, so the growing plants would receive much more sunlight. These large areas had to be covered with automatic shutters that closed each time a picture was taken in order to have the same amount of photographic light just as in the basement studio. These large shutters like giant Venetian blinds worked independently of each other and automatically followed the sun so that the louvers all remained parallel to the rays of light as it moved across the sky. In this way they created the least amount of shadow and let in the maximum amount of direct sunlight. The north wall was solid and was painted sky blue to act as a photographic backgound for the subjects being photographed. Sky blue seemed to be the most natural color for a background and made it easier to match backgrounds of time-lapse pictures taken in the greenhouse with regular shots made out in the field. The new greenhouse also had more head room so tall corn and small trees could be grown inside. This made it possible to start taking time-lapse pictures of many more new subjects that also created many more new problems.

When the new plastic greenhouse was completed to the point where time-lapse cameras could be started, the Ferry-Morse Seed Company wanted a time-lapse picture of one of their varieties of morning glories. This certainly appeared to be one of the simplest assignments I had ever undertaken. The results of the earlier experiments with growing corn and other plants under plastic as contrasted to those grown under glass had been so outstanding that I visualized extra fine morning glories bursting into bloom.

I planted some seeds in another small lean-to glass greenhouse by the garage. This was a good place to start some subjects and grow them until they were ready to take time-lapse pictures of them. In this way valuable space in the new plastic greenhouse could be conserved and used only for plants actually being photographed.

As the morning glory vines neared the budding stage, I moved them from the glass house to the plastic house. Everything went well until the buds were just ready to open. Then bud after bud would collapse without opening. This was terribly discouraging after all the experimenting done with different plastics. How could I justify the substantially higher cost of having built an all-plastic greenhouse, only to find that my morning glories positively would not open, even though the buds seemed to develop quite normally. This was perplexing, to say the least. Could it be the result of having moved or changed the growing conditions during the bud development period? Any such slight change of conditions should have been all for the better. Nevertheless I started more seeds right in the plastic greenhouse where they could be photographed and nothing would have to be moved or changed in the slightest during the entire growing period. Again though, exactly the same as before, the buds collapsed just when they should have opened. I could remember having seen morning glories growing in glass greenhouses with flowers in full bloom, so everything was cleared out of the glass greenhouse. Then cameras, lights, timers, shutters—the whole works were moved in again, and more morning glories were started from seed. This all took time, and the summer was just about over, but with any luck there should still be time for one more crop of morning glories. Though still disappointed about the results in the plastic greenhouse, the morning glories and cameras were all installed in the old glass lean-to alongside of the garage. By slightly swallowing my pride and with a little luck, perhaps this picture might still be completed during the current year. But—as the buds reached the point again when they should open, the same thing happened—no luck.

Besides having a rather complete library of film showing morning glory buds collapsing, the fact that the buds still refused to open in the glass greenhouse indicated perhaps the problem was not with the plastic after all. This in itself was quite gratifying even though I still did not have the needed pictures nor any real clue as to why the morning glory buds persisted in collapsing without opening. One thing learned right at the start in trying to take time-lapse pictures was not to photograph plants out of their normal growing season. It is hard enough with most plants, if not practically impossible, to grow them at all out of season, let alone trying to get flowers worth photographing. People are not interested in looking at a poor picture, even though it may be of the impossible. This project had to go down in the records as unfinished.

Meanwhile during the very early days of television, I had been asked to appear on several programs and show some time-lapse pictures of flowers. During the early days when television stations were having difficulty obtaining suitable material for their increasing hours of air time, the program director of one of the first Chicago stations called me on the phone. Could I bring some of my old films in and help him out for half an hour on a Sunday afternoon? This was something new and somewhat of a challenge, too. Everything went quite well, and I was invited back the following Sunday, and the Sunday after that, and so on. After only a few Sundays of helping the program director fill a half hour of time, I was greatly surprised to see my name listed in the paper as a local TV personality. This was taking an entirely different point of view of the matter of merely helping to fill a half hour's time until something better could be arranged for. Nevertheless, the Sunday half hours continued, and even expanded to include my participation either live or on

TV set representing interior of old tool shed for weekly program "How Does Your Garden Grow," first program to be broadcast in color from Chicago.

film in a number of established programs including "The Home Show," "Today," "Out On The Farm," and "Disneyland," in addition to my own regular weekly program that was to be called "How Does Your Garden Grow." This required a new subject each week which necessitated some scouting around to find interesting material.

Late that fall when the morning glories were causing so much trouble, one program was on the subject of chrysanthemums. In addition to trying to explain everything from planting to picking the flowers, I always attempted to give some additional interesting information. This might include something about the origin, or how the particular flower found its way to this country, or how they are raised commercially.

There is a very interesting story about how chrysanthemums are grown out of season. They are now available in full bloom every month of the year. Most varieties of chrysanthemums ordinarily set their buds toward late summer as the daylight hours shorten. It has now been proven that some plants such as wheat, require a certain number of hours of sunlight before the plants will head up, but with chrysanthemums it is just the reverse. The plants of course need sunlight to grow, but it is the lengthening of the dark or night period that controls the setting of their flower buds. When the length of the dark period amounts to approximately ten and a half hours or more, the buds begin to develop. It is now common practice for commercial growers to cover their chrysanthemum plants with black cloth suspended on wires or iron pipe frames. During the long daylight hours of the spring months, chrysanthemums are covered over about four-thirty in the afternoon, and not uncovered until about eight-thirty the next morning. The effect is to prematurely or artificially lengthen the night period, and the chrysanthemums set their buds and come into flower ahead of their normal blooming period. Likewise, if ordinary electric lights are turned on in the evening as the days grow shorter, and the night period held under ten and one half hours, the plants will keep on growing taller, and delay setting their buds.

This sounded a little like a possible clue to my morning glory trouble. Maybe the photographic lights going on every few minutes for five seconds all night long were interrupting the normal dark period. My morning glories had no problem of setting buds; it was just that they wouldn't open. The light only affected the setting of buds on chrysanthemums, and after they were once set and showing a little color, they would continue to develop regardless of the length of the day or night period.

I was also trying to take time-lapse pictures of poinsettias for my Christmas TV program, and ran into similar problems. The poinsettia flowers—that is, the colorful bracts—literally stopped in their tracks as soon as I started photographing them. It made no difference how far along the flower was. I heard a story from Honolulu that the Chamber of Commerce there on the island ran into the same difficulty when an attempt was made to turn floodlights on some of the poinsettias in one of the parks. It is also known that a street-light, too near a greenhouse of poinsettias, will cause all kinds of problems as far as their not blooming is concerned. Commercial poinsettia growers have also quite recently started to control the light and dark period to bring their plants into peak bloom right on Christmas Day. Poinsettias are another flower that set their buds and come into bloom as the dark night hours grow longer during the fall and winter period. Accordingly as the length of daylight shortens earlier in the season the further north you go, poinsettias also bloom earlier up north. In the Chicago area they come into full bloom around the first part of December, and florists in the past have had difficulty in holding the plants for the Christmas trade. Now it is customary to turn the lights on in the greenhouses for approximately two hours at midnight for a ten-day period commencing September twenty-ninth. This is when poinsettias ordinarily begin to set their buds in the latitude of Chicago. By turning the lights on and interrupting the night period, the process of setting buds is delayed, and now the height of the blooming period is attained right on Christmas Day. In this way the plants are much fresher and will last longer in the home.

All this seemed to tie into my morning glory problem, but just how was the real question. Nothing seemed to fit exactly, but nothing further could be done with morning glories anyway until spring. The time went quickly, and soon it was time to plant more seed. When the first buds were ready to open, I had morning glories all over the place—in the plastic greenhouse, in the basement studio under the big skylight, in the glass lean-to greenhouse, and this time also outdoors on the garden fence. The morning glories outdoors bloomed fine, but all the ones indoors being photographed still insisted on collapsing just when they should open. I tried cutting down the intensity of the photographic lights to the point where pictures could no longer be taken, and still they collapsed. Then I got an idea, and accidentally something happened all at the same time that gave me the answer. The name morning glory is slightly misleading. I had assumed that they open to their full glory with the morning sun as it rises. But one morning when I was up well before sunrise, I noticed the flowers outdoors were already open. In other words, morning glories are a night-blooming flower. Interesting, but still, so are iris and others that presented no problem photographing. The night-blooming cereus readily opens only at night even though photographic or other bright electric lights are turned on in the same room. I decided to try something and stopped taking pictures in the glass greenhouse altogether. That night the morning glories opened normally. The next night I hung an extension cord with a light on the garden fence where the morning glories had been blooming normally. It was connected so that it would flash on each time a picture was taken in the plastic greenhouse. The next morning the outside morning glory buds were all collapsed within a perfect circle around the electric light. This showed definitely the problem was clearly due to the photographic lights interrupting the night period.

What happened accidentally at this same time came as a result of thinking about the poor old budget again. Expenses on this subject for quite some time had to be charged to the research and experience account, so I was quite conscious of piling up additional film costs. There happened to be a short end of unused daylight type color film which I thought might as well be used up. Ordinarily I used commercial Kodachrome, which is color-balanced to regular photo-flood lamps. As all photographers who take any color pictures know, daylight film is balanced to sunlight which is somewhat bluer than ordinary artificial lights. Indoors it is necessary to use either a blue filter over the lens with daylight type Kodachrome film or special bluish lights. This time I used blue lights instead of the regular

Bottom row—morning glory bud bursts into full bloom when additional blue filters were placed over blue photo-flood lights. This filtered red wave lengths from photographic lights that interrupted the dark period of flower that ordinarily blooms at night.

Top row shows 16 mm enlargements of morning glory buds collapsing.

Center picture — morning glory bud opens part way when blue photo-flood was used with daylight color film.

ones without giving it a second thought. The next morning when checking the morning glories, I really did give it a lot of thought, as several of the buds had opened half way for the first time. What was it? The only possible difference was the use of blue photo-floods to go with the daylight film. Actually several of them had been used, and the bluish light was considerably brighter than the regular lights that wouldn't work at all. Could it be because the light was a little blue? Maybe wave lengths of light had something to do with these morning glory buds. That night I put additional blue filters over the slightly blue photo-floods. The next morning the morning glories were open full and perfectly. This was surprising, to say the least. The pictures were, of course, way too blue, but after a little experimenting with red filters over the camera lens, I could get a pretty well-balanced color picture. The blue filters in effect were filtering out the red wave lengths from the photographic light. It was the red wave lengths of the spectrum in the photographic lights interrupting the normal dark period at night that was the controlling factor in preventing the morning glory buds from opening.

Another equally troublesome subject was in the works at the same time. This was a time-lapse picture of the growth of a pumpkin, for Walt Disney's "SECRETS OF LIFE." This project presented various new problems, particularly in regard to the sex life of a pumpkin. I might explain that a pumpkin is a member of the cucumber family, which includes most of the squashes and melons, and is known as a monoecious type plant. This means that it has separate male and female flowers on the same plant.

To begin with, I planted a pumpkin under the skylight in the basement studio. Next I hung some fluorescent lights over it in order to supplement the natural daylight and approximate full summer sunlight intensity. The pumpkin vine grew well, but all the female or pistillate pumpkin producing flowers turned brown and dropped off very soon after they formed. The staminate or male pollen producing flowers grew vigorously but were of little use all by themselves. Needless to say, no pumpkins developed so I had to try it again the next year. Meanwhile the fluorescent light tubes had burned out, and had to be replaced. The hardware store was out of the regular kind of fluorescent tubes used the previous year and rather then waiting for them to be re-ordered, I took some daylight white tubes. These were generally less desirable and in less demand, as their slightly bluish color made ladies' lipstick look a ghastly purple.

I planted more pumpkin seeds the second year under the new fluorescent lights and watched carefully. It was possible to plant them indoors under the skylight ahead of the regular outdoor planting time in order to get an early start. The vine seemed to grow just as well. The flower buds began forming, but this time all the male flowers turned brown and dropped off, and the female flowers developed vigorously.

Thus for the second time after having photographed a vine every five minutes over a period of months from the time the seed was planted until it had grown over fifteen feet, I was confronted with the problem of all flowers of only one sex. This time a perfect female or pumpkin-producing flower which I figured would open the next day, and nothing but pictures of the male flower—and a year old at that.

The next day the flower was open and would have to be pollinated before closing that night if it was to produce a pumpkin. In this delicate situation I decided to call my friend, Dr. Harold Tukey, head of the Department of Horticulture at Michigan State University. I asked him if he had any pumpkins growing at that time of year in the department's experimental greenhouses, and also if it might be possible to use any kind of artificial hormones. Dr. Tukey had no pumpkins and advised that real pumpkin pollen would be necessary under these circumstances.

Next I called Dr. Dorsey at the University of Illinois, but he said that he was sorry he had no pumpkin pollen at the moment either.

Then I called Dr. Julian Miller at Louisiana State University. Dr. Miller had been very helpful on one previous occasion in settling a disputed question as to which end of a sweet potato is "up" when planting one in a jar of water on the kitchen window sill. (He advised that this differs with various varieties and that the problem can be avoided by planting the potato on its side.) Possibly the pumpkins might be blooming in Louisiana, but Dr. Miller told me there would be none for a week or ten days. This would be much too late for my beautiful pumpkin flower which was now in full bloom.

Maybe the pumpkins might be in bloom a little farther south, so I called Mr. Deatrick of the Flagler Hydroponic Gardens in Miami. I asked him if he could look around Florida to see if there were any male pumpkin flowers in bloom. After explaining the urgency of the situation, he said he would see what he could do. He called me back a little later in the morning, saying that he had spread the word. By noon an urgent appeal for pumpkin pollen had been published in the early edition of the Miami paper and broadcast on the radio so my beautiful little lady flower wouldn't die a spinster. By two o'clock that afternoon a lady living in Miami called in that she had a pumpkin vine with male flowers in bloom and offered it in this emergency. While sitting at my desk wondering how I could get a male flower or at least some pollen before dark, the telephone rang. It was the vice president of Eastern Air Lines. He had heard of the plight of my lady pumpkin flower in full bloom and offered their facilities in this emergency. He arranged to have the whole pumpkin vine dug up and placed aboard a non-stop plane to Chicago. I dashed out to the airport and waited for the plane. Soon it was announced and I was escorted out on the field. Newspaper photographers and reporters had gathered, but no one really knew who the important celebrity was. From all the commotion it obviously had to be a movie star or foreign royalty. No one would believe me when I told them it was King Pumpkin, or perhaps they just didn't understand. The passengers were all held on the plane until the pumpkin was unloaded and delivered to me. I rushed it out to my time-lapse studio, where I introduced it to the lady in waiting. Now I am being called Uncle John by a lot of little pumpkins and particularly the one that starred in Walt Disney's "SECRETS OF LIFE."

Actually there may not be too many people interested in the sex life of a pumpkin, but the fact that either male or female flowers can be brought forth by controlling slight variations in color or wave length of light opens up some interesting possibilities for investigation. The next step will be to shade various parts of the plant from the fluorescent light, and try to find out whether the control comes through the leaves or the flower itself, and just what part of the flower at what stage of development; and how long must the exposure to light be.

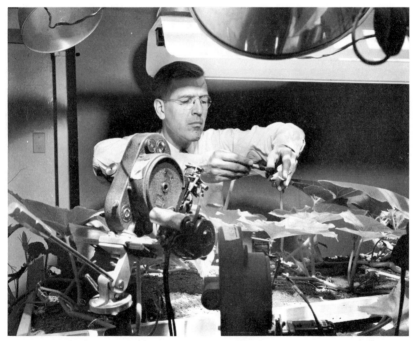

Using a camel's hair brush to pollinate the pumpkin flower with pollen received from Florida. Note fluorescent light fixture hanging overhead.

Staminate or male pollen producing flowers grew vigorously when cool white fluorescent tubes were used to supplement sunlight. . . .

But all the pistillate or female pumpkin producing flowers turned yellow at a very early stage of development.

Soon they turned black, dried up and dropped off the vine. The result—no pumpkins.

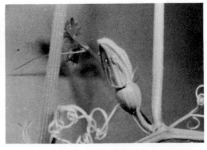

The following year daylight white fluorescent tubes were used to supplement the natural sunlight. This time the pistillate or female pumpkin producing flowers grew vigorously. . . .

But at the same early stage of development, all the staminate or male pollen producing flowers turned yellow.

They too dried up and dropped off the vine. Result—no pumpkin pollen.

This picture was taken later in the season outdoors and shows how the bees normally pollinate the pumpkin flower. However, there were neither bees nor pollen in the basement time-lapse studio.

Pumpkin develops rapidly after flower has been pollinated with pollen received from Florida. Note small weak staminate flower which failed to mature.

Pumpkin continues to grow larger. Note remains of flower still evident on pumpkin at opposite end from stem.

Here is the fully ripened pumpkin that was used in Walt Disney's film SECRETS OF LIFE.

Chapter 8

Double Trouble

The same year my pumpkin vine was producing all male flowers, I was also having problems with an apple that refused to ripen. Walt Disney wanted to include a picture of the growth of an apple in the same film, "SECRETS OF LIFE." It was hardly practical to move an apple tree down into the basement, so I built a complete time-lapse studio in miniature on a scaffold by the apple tree in the front yard. This was constructed so that there was a glass window or skylight in the top of a large box. It was equipped with shutters that would close to keep the sunlight out momentarily each time an individual frame was exposed on the moving picture film. It also contained the necessary timing equipment to operate three cameras, the overhead shutters, and photographic lights. Two automatic thermostats controlled an electric heater and ventilating fan to maintain the proper temperature in the box and prevent over-heating in the direct sunlight.

A branch of the apple tree that had the best looking buds was selected, and the large box-like time-lapse studio was placed around it. Both the subject and equipment were then completely protected from wind and rain. The apple branch was fastened securely so it would not move during the time required for the dormant bud to develop into a nice juicy red apple. The entire tree had to be battened down with many wires and turnbuckles to hold it rigid and motionless during a severe thunder or wind storm.

Everything was all completed and ready to go about the middle of March. The switch was turned on and the project officially started. If all went well, this picture would be completed by apple harvest time in October. The cameras had to be checked at least once each day and a careful watch maintained for any insects or disease that might harm the apple. All did go well for a while. The buds opened on schedule and were large and healthy looking. Pollen from several other varieties of apple trees was collected and a small camel hair brush used to hand pollinate the blossoms being photographed. Ordinarily this is done by the honeybees, and frequently commercial orchard growers hire beekeepers to bring their hives into the orchards during the blossom period.

Bees have an interesting way of communication amongst themselves that helps them do a thorough job. When a scout bee finds a good supply of blossoms, she returns to the hive and does what is known as the honey dance. She (for the lady bees do all the work) repeatedly runs a short distance on the surface of the honeycomb in the hive where the other bees can see her. As she runs, she also violently wiggle-waggles her posterior end. The direction of her short runs in relation to the position of the sun is thought to indicate the location of the newly discovered flowers. The number of wiggle-waggles tells the distance from the hives. Oddly enough, the greater number of waggles means the flowers are nearby and is the way the bees attract the greatest amount of attention of other workers to the closest supply of nectar.

There was no problem in hand-pollinating the blossoms in the box, but I needed an extreme close-up picture of the bee itself on a blossom, and this was not easy. The bees never stayed on any blossom long enough to set up a camera and focus it properly.

Bee collecting nectar from apple blossom. As bees and other insects travel from blossom to blossom, they also carry pollen from one flower to another.

Upon returning to the hive, a scout bee does the honey dance to indicate location of flowers to other worker bees.

The blossom also had to remain perfectly motionless, as the field
and depth of focus on such an extreme close-up were very criti-
cal. Finally I fastened a twig with a freshly opened apple

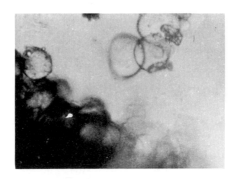

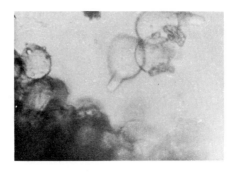

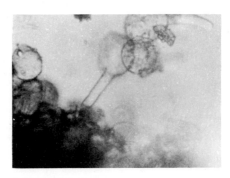

Sequence showing growth of pollen tube as it penetrates stigma of flower. Protoplasmic
contents of pollen flow through tube to fertilize ovary of flower.

blossom on one end of a board with a sky-blue background. At
the other end I mounted my camera. They were both so arranged
that I could carry the entire unit around, and the camera would
remain focused right on the best looking blossom. Now all that
I thought was necessary was to place the blossom end of this
contraption near the opening of a beehive, and surely the bees
would take advantage of this wonderful opportunity. However,
they completely ignored both me and the blossoms. I kept poking
it a little closer to the hive opening where the bees were streaming in and out. I moved it around and wiggled it to attract
their attention. Suddenly as though someone had given a signal
or command, the bees all came at me like dive bombers. They
got in my hair and buzzed and swarmed all over me, but sur-
prisingly enough, not one stung me. I got the idea though that
my presence was not appreciated near their hive and quickly
retreated. Then I noticed the bees were working in a tree in
another yard nearby. When I placed the end of the board with
the apple blossom on it up in this tree, the bees would accept it
there, and I was able to get a good close-up of the bee at work
collecting nectar and pollen.

Soon the blossoms were dropping, and the small apples were
beginning to take shape. As the pictures later showed, apples
grow during the daytime and relax at night. The effect on the
screen was like someone blowing up a balloon a little at a time.
During the entire summer I continued to watch the development
of the several apples on the branch inside the time-lapse box
and compare them with the other apples on the same tree that
were out in the open. Everything seemed to be going along
perfectly normally until all the apples not in the time-lapse box
began to mature and turn a nice red color. The apples inside the
box being photographed were still green and continued to grow
larger and larger. The increased size was fine, but Walt Disney
wanted the picture to show the apple turning red. Spraying
the apples with various chemical products that were supposed
to make fruit develop better color had no effect. The apples
still remained green. At last the apples outside my box began
dropping off the tree. Inside the box they kept on growing
until the weather was so cold that they froze solid—and still
a disgustingly healthy looking green color.

This was another disappointment and also a very important
subject. There was no real clue as to what could have been the
trouble. Down came all the equipment, and down came the
unsightly box from the apple tree by the front door of the
house. I thought about this all winter and discussed it with
many friends and experts on growing apples. The best thing
to do was to try it again the next year on a different variety
of apple. To make doubly sure of getting a picture on the second

Miniature time-lapse studios mounted on scaffolds to record time-lapse pictures of growth
of an apple.

try, two scaffolds were built by two other varieties of apple
trees. On each one went a big box with all the equipment.
I watched and waited. The blossoms opened and were hand-
pollinated again. The small apples began to take shape. Day by
day, all summer long, I waited and watched them grow larger.
If you think it takes a long time for a kettle to boil while you
are watching it, try watching apples grow for two years.

In the past no difficulty had been encountered with the ripening process or coloration in making time-lapse pictures of many other subjects including peppers, tomatoes, and various fruits and vegetables from bud to full maturity. Tomatoes will turn red even when picked green and stored in complete darkness. The tomato though has sort of a split personality. Botanically speaking, it is a fruit because it develops from a flower as the result of pollination and contains seeds. Legally speaking, it is a vegetable according to a ruling on a tax case handed down by the Supreme Court of the United States.

As the season progressed and the time of year rolled around again, I watched faint traces of red color begin to show in all the apples in all the trees except those being photographed in my two time-lapse boxes. There the green color persisted, and again they continued to grow larger and larger. I double-checked the temperature controls in both boxes and found only approximately 2 degrees variation from outside. Taking into consideration the wide fluctuation of temperatures from day to day and variations between daytime and night time, this slight difference certainly could not be enough to matter. What could be preventing the apples in the box from maturing?

Finally in desperation I removed the glass from the window over the apples and replaced it with the new plastic material that let more of all the sun's rays penetrate and particularly the ultraviolet and shorter wave lengths. These are the ones that ordinary glass will not transmit. Within two days the apples in the boxes were showing a nice red color, and for once I was real happy to see red. The picture was completed just in time to be included in Walt Disney's film, "SECRETS OF LIFE." They also proved that the maturing and ripening process of an apple can be prevented by filtering certain wave lengths of energy from normal sunlight.

Time-lapse sequence shows growth of apple used in Walt Disney's film, SECRETS OF LIFE.

Chapter 9

Contemporary Influences

For quite a few years I used the waltzing primroses as the grand finale to my lecture film. Everyone always seemed to enjoy it, and as many times as I had seen the flowers dance around and take a bow, they never became tiresome to watch. Five years was a long time to spend on one short sequence, and it should last a long time. As new pictures were completed, I would replace some of the old ones in my lecture film. The waltzing flowers though were like a trade mark, and to leave them out was unthinkable.

But times change, and the old must make way for the new. At last one day the inevitable came to pass. Two of my sons in all seriousness and good faith tactfully tried to explain to me that the waltzing flowers had seen their best days and were getting out of date. They thought I would do much better to keep more abreast of the time and introduce some rock and roll or dixieland rhythm. It was hard to visualize primroses doing the rock and roll, but gradually the idea sunk in. Maybe some other kind of flowers would respond faster. It required two or three days for a primrose leaf to wilt down and then revive, but many flowers would open and close their petals in response to light and heat alone, and much faster than primroses wilting. The accepted theory was that the petals of flowers opened and closed from more or less of a mechanical response to light and heat. If the timers on the skylight controls were adjusted, it would be possible to artificially shorten the day and night periods to just a few hours. The individual pictures could be taken at shorter intervals, and perhaps several days work could be accomplished in one ordinary 24-hour period. The day and night controls on the thermostat could also be adjusted so that the temperature would correspond to the shorter light and dark periods. The air-conditioning equipment would cool the studio down 10 degrees while the skylight shutters remained closed to simulate the cooler night air. There was no doubt about it now, the dancing flowers were going to keep up with the times. I would make the petals open and close three or four times during one ordinary day.

My neighbor's son had a trumpet, and I had heard him practicing on it for the last ten years or more. In fact he and some of his friends played together and had a pretty good dixieland band. I didn't realize how good they really were until they came over to the old tool shed and played for me. I asked for several selections including "Tiger Rag," explaining some tiger lilies might dance to this tune. They all looked at each other with a peculiar expression but then started in to play, and things really warmed up out in the old tool shed.

The music was recorded on magnetic tape, and then re-recorded onto an optical film track so the various vibrations could be analyzed. The motion could then be plotted for the tiger lilies growth. A sound track can be pulled through a sound reader so that the sounds of different instruments can be heard by ear and marked on the film. However, after studying the sound track for a while, it is not too difficult to visually read the characteristic vibrations and pick up the beat of the rhythm as well as the different instruments. My procedure was to number each individual frame on the picture part of the film and then sketch the position the flowers had to be in at that particular point. Next the length of time necessary for the plants and flowers to reach that stage of development had to be estimated. Then the number of frames along the sound track between the various points of growth development were counted. A little simple arithmetic, and the automatic timers were set. All that remained to be done was to grow the plants so the flower buds would reach the predetermined stage of development on schedule. In theory it is quite simple, but in practice a little experience is quite helpful.

Certain flowers like roses, peonies and tulips open their petals during the daytime and close them at night. Many other flowers open only once and stay open until they fade away. Another group open during the night time and close their petals during the daytime. Then there are those that open for the first time during the night and stay open. Four O'Clocks open at the end

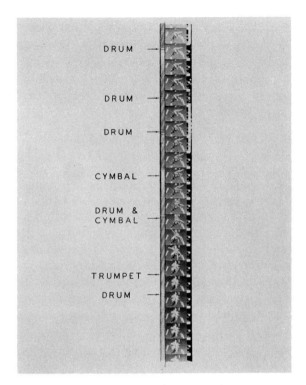

DRUM —

DRUM —

DRUM —

CYMBAL —

DRUM &
CYMBAL —

TRUMPET —
DRUM —

Section of film showing opening of tiger lily with sound track. Vibrations on sound track are identified according to the sounds of the instruments they represent. Sound recorder converts sound vibrations into light vibrations which are photographed right on the film.

of the day along towards dusk, and tiger lilies are in the group that open at the end of the dark night period as the eastern horizon begins to show the first faint glimmers of light. The opening and closing habits of different flowers are one more factor to contend with when adjusting the timing mechanisms that control the cameras, lights, shutters, temperature and automatic watering devices used in making flowers dance in time to music.

Such a project requires a little advance planning particularly with regard to the plants that must be started the previous year or grown for several years to become well established. Eventually the day for action approaches, and everything must be checked and double-checked. Provisions for extra lights are important in case of a cloudy day. Extra plants must be grown and be in readiness in case the first flower bud does not open up perfectly. More plants must be grown to bloom several days later as a safety factor in case of a power failure or other difficulty of a similar serious nature. Every possible emergency must be planned for particularly when a year or two's preparatory work is at stake.

At last came the day when the flowers would start dancing to dixieland rhythm. When the pictures were finished and projected on the screen, the action must coincide exactly with the rhythm of the music. While the pictures are being taken, the flowers of course do not hear any music, as this has already been recorded. The speeded-up action necessitated by dixieland rhythm means that one single movement of the petals must be accomplished in two hours now instead of twelve as in the past. This faster action still cannot be seen at normal speed as the flowers grow, but through time-lapse photography, the flowers when projected on the moving picture screen move about in rhythm with the music.

Again to begin with, everything worked as planned. The skylight shutters opened at sunrise, and the heat came on as scheduled. The petals on the flowers all opened up perfectly. With the increased rate of taking individual exposures, the normal full day's work was accomplished by 10 o'clock in the morning. As planned, the skylight shutters closed, the heat went off, and the air conditioning started. All the flowers closed their petals just as they would normally do during the night. At the continued increased rate of picture taking, the night's work was all completed by 12 o'clock noon. Automatically the skylight shutters opened again, the air conditioning shut off, and the heat turned on. The sun was bright and clear and at its maximum intensity. The closed flowers were in full direct sunlight. This would most likely make them open a little faster than the early morning sun, so I made a slight change in the timing schedule, as this was one thing that had been completely overlooked. I watched closely and waited. Ten minutes went by, and nothing happened. Fifteen minutes, a half hour, and still the petals remained in their closed position. I changed the timing mechanism from the faster schedule to an extremely slow one, but by now everything was completely off schedule. The action of the flowers would already be out of synchronization with the pre-recorded music. This group of flower subjects was spoiled, but perhaps I could use them to experiment with and make them open with additional artificial light and higher room temperature. Then I would be ready with the second set of plants that would be coming into bloom in a few days.

Nothing would make the petals open again, and I found out that they would not open a second time until the plants had gone through a full night period of darkness without having their sleep interrupted. In view of the seasonal blooming period of many flowers, it is not always possible to experiment with them in advance. Much of the preparatory work must be started months ahead of blooming period, otherwise a full year will have to pass from the time that experiments can be made and the next season rolls around when the pictures can be taken. In this case I was so certain that the petals of the flowers would respond to the light and dark periods, that I hardly gave it a second thought. All the information available on this subject indicated that there should be no trouble in making the flowers respond.

Later when the reserve flowers came into bloom, I exposed all the individual frames of the petals in any one particular stage of development in quick succession. It was necessary to skip a number of frames and leave them unexposed until the flower reached various stages of development. Then I would go back and fill in the unexposed frames and thus be able to give the effect of the flower opening and closing whereas actually the petals only opened once and would fade away without ever closing. In effect it would be like showing a picture of a flower opening on the screen and then reversing the projector and running it backwards again and repeating this same procedure to look as though the flower opened and closed several times. Instead the same effect was obtained by photographing the proper stages of development in the respective locations along the film to record a number of openings and reverse action closings.

The method of taking these pictures is possibly of some interest, but the real significance of the preliminary failure of this project of trying to speed up the opening and closing of the petals of flowers to the rhythm of dixieland music is of some possible importance. I believe it shows that the response of the petals in opening and closing is not of a mechanical nature but is tied into the principles of photochemistry. Certain chemical changes apparently take place during the dark night period while the plant seems to sleep. The petals will not open in response to the energy of the light until these chemical changes have taken place. I suspect that the plant produces a chemical substance during the dark hours, but there is the possibility also that the plant could be disposing of certain wastes or byproduct chemical substances accumulated during the daytime. Either way there seems to be a close correlation with human sleep. If the chemical produced by the plant during the night period could be isolated and produced synthetically, it would make possible an interesting experiment. Could this chemical substance be administered to the plant in such a way that the petals would respond to light repeatedly without the plant having its uninterrupted night sleep? If so, then would the same principle work with animals and humans, and again if this proves to be the case, then this might add helpful knowledge regarding such drugs as the new tranquilizers. Carrying this even further, it might even be possible some day to make a pill that would be the equivalent of a good eight or twelve hours' sleep. Sounds incredible, but no more so than a trip to the moon.

Chapter 10

Interesting Similarities Between Growth Reactions of Plants and Animals

---

We have seen how some spore plants also developed seeds, and how the ginkgo tree was a step in the transition from pine to the more recent broadleaf trees.

The duck bill platypus is a similar transition in animal life. It is a small aquatic mammal that lays eggs but also nurses its young. It has a bill like a duck, thick dark fur of an animal, and five webbed toes, whereas reptiles and birds have but three.

Today new scientific findings are constantly being reported that fill in missing gaps in the evolution of modern man. Additional information recently reported reveals the similarity in certain basic cell structure between human cells and a primitive type of seaweed. Whether or not animals including man have evolved from plant life or not, there are remarkable similarities in the development of each that would seem to indicate the same divine power was working behind the scenes at the controls in both instances. The same principles of camouflage are utilized by many plants as well as by insects and animals for self-preservation. The spines of cactus and the quills of a porcupine offer the same kind of protection. Certain odors of plants attract or repel insects that carry pollen from one plant to another. Similar odors of animals work in the same way during the mating season.

Both plants and animals respond in many similar ways to light. Some mink ranchers are now making their mink produce heavy winter pelts in mid-summer by using the exact same method of lengthening the night period that the florists use to bring chrysanthemums into bloom out of season. Light is the primary controlling factor rather than temperature. This is how animals develop heavy fur ahead of the cold weather instead of later as a result of it.

It is now known the lengthening night period causes certain glandular changes in birds that are responsible for their seasonal migration. People in the poultry business turn lights on in the hen houses at night to lengthen the daylight period so the hens lay more eggs. Originally it was thought this merely kept the hens awake longer, but more recent research has proven that increased egg production is attained as a result of the light reacting through the chicken's eye on its pituitary gland. Farmers for a long time have used red celluloid spectacles over the eyes of chickens to reduce cannibalistic tendencies.

Most of the principal life functions of animals and humans can be traced back into primitive plant life such as the way humans breathe with their lungs is a big improvement over the way plants breathe through their leaves. The circulation system is a big improvement over the way sap flows through the leaves and stems and roots of plants, and the principles of reproduction of animals are similar but a vast improvement over the pollination of flowers and development of seeds. However, the most important life function of plants is the process of photosynthesis, the growth response to the energy of sunlight. It is the essence of life itself but has always been thought to stop with plant life and not carry over to animal life. The only benefit to animal life is supposed to be received through the eating of plants.

One thing the taking of time-lapse pictures of flowers taught me was how many exceptions there are to all the rules of nature. Nevertheless, it seems logical that the most fundamental basic life principle of all should carry over into animal life as do so many other less important functions.

One film I made from many of the pictures I took while traveling about the country was entitled, OUR CHANGING WORLD. It stressed the orderly progression of the creation of the earth and development of life from the beginning of time down to the present. The conclusion of the film illustrates how much more rapidly recent developments have taken place on our earth and includes an interesting comparison between a present day giant Sequoia tree and what we think of as man's present civilization in regard to time. It reads as follows:

"We have seen plants of every color and description, all kinds and colors of fish, reptiles, birds, and animals. We have seen the succession of ever higher forms of life that have lived supreme in their time. Today it is man—men of different colors. Is there any reason to believe that present man represents the highest form in the development of life on this earth, or in time to come will some still more advanced creature look back on present man as merely a transition animal or stepping-stone in the process of development on our changing world? Maybe man's future development will come in further advancement of his mind, or possibly his soul. Have you ever stopped to realize what a comparatively short time man has existed on this earth?

"Imprinted in the stone of a French cave is the footprint of primitive man, left there in the soft mud about fifteen thousand years ago, during the time of the last great glacier. The story of modern man is one of incredibly fast development, and can well be illustrated by the life-span of a single giant Sequoia tree, one of the oldest living things in the world today. Several of these giant trees in California are estimated to be about four thousand years old. This would mean they started to grow about the time that Jacob, son of Abraham, led his people and their flocks from the land of Caanan to seek refuge in Egypt. During the life of these trees, many empires have risen and fallen— the Egyptian, Roman, Greek and others that today are classified as ancient history. Why have all these empires crumbled? Why cannot man maintain what he has achieved? The answer is not easy, but the same social and political trends seem to have prevailed with each empire's decline. The general philosophy of men changed from that of each individual supporting the state to that of the state caring for each individual. More and more people were supported by government payrolls and social security, leaving fewer and fewer supporting government. Taxes rose to high proportions. The cost of government at home and the cost of maintaining armies of occupation in conquered lands became too great. Historians also tell us that other trends preceding the fall of these ancient empires were the breaking up of the home as a family unit, together with a tendency to ignore the church. But though empires rise and fall, these big trees live on.

"Perhaps this calendar will help explain the relative time of the various geological periods of the earth's history. If the time since the earth's beginning until today was represented by one year, then the accumulation of the various gases would have taken place during the month of January. February would have represented the burning period, and March, the formation of a thin outer crust. By April, the surface would have cooled sufficiently to permit water to fill the oceans. In May, the most primitive one-celled plants and animals would have made their appearance. During June—continued great crustal disturbances, volcanic activity and formation of some of the oldest mountain ranges. July would have seen the first blue-green algae. Seaweed began to grow in August. In September, two-thirds of North America were still under water. During October there was further great volcanic activity, and important deposits of copper, gold, nickel and silver were laid down. The great coal-making period took place in November. The first week in December was the age of reptiles. Birds appeared during the second week, and the Rocky Mountains and first modern plants during the third. By December 26th, mammals were dominating the earth; 27th, elephants; 28th, the Alps were formed; primitive man appeared on the 29th, and showed considerable development by the 30th. On the morning of the 31st, he was already using simple stone implements; by afternoon he had begun using bronze; and by evening, iron. At five minutes before midnight, the last glacier melted away, and modern man was developing rapidly. One minute before midnight saw the end of the Egyptian Empire. Thirty seconds later the Roman Empire was falling, and in ten seconds more, Christ was born. The Clock is now striking midnight, and only five seconds left. Columbus discovers America. One second left. The Declaration of Independence is signed, and during this last second of the year, man has built our present civilization, has cut down our forests to make lumber, has taken coal and minerals from the earth to build our great cities, ships, automobiles, streamliners, airplanes and space rockets. New inventions are coming in split-second succession. We are entering the Atomic Age."

After each showing of the film, many people would say how much they enjoyed seeing the flowers open and die away, but I will never forget one time out in a small western town, a big burly, rough-and tough-looking cowboy came up to me and said my pictures made him feel like turning around and saying, "Beg your pardon," whenever he stepped on a wild flower.

Chapter 11

Photocrinology—The Effect of Light on The Glandular System

One day as the result of my TV programs, a letter came in the mail from a biology teacher in Chicago, stating that he was doing research work involving fish eggs and wanted to take some time-lapse pictures. I was delighted to be able to help and moved one of my time-lapse units right into his laboratory where he had quite a few tropical fish. When the time-lapse picture-taking was well along and he seemed quite pleased with the results, I suggested we hang some of the different fluorescent lights used on the pumpkins over two or three of the fish aquariums. This was, of course, ridiculous, but as I had loaned him considerable photographic equipment for his project, he agreed to the experiment with the lights.

No time was lost in setting up the light fixtures over the aquariums. Each fixture held two 40-watt fluorescent tubes and was placed ten inches above the surface of the water. A time clock was set to turn them on at six o'clock in the morning and off at six in the evening. To start with, three different types of fluorescent tubes, cool white, daylight white, and pink were used. The aquariums were not located near any window, so the fish were being subjected entirely to fluorescent light. The first thing that happened was that the fish completely stopped laying any eggs. This was not good because the biology teacher needed the eggs for his work. On the other hand, it did indicate that light possibly did have some effect on the fish. After two weeks the light intensity was cut in half by removing one of the fluorescent tubes from each fixture. Still no egg production. Gradually we shortened the length of time the lights were left on. When the duration was down to eight hours a day, the fish began producing more eggs. These were carefully collected and kept in a special tank until they hatched.

Ordinarily the sex of certain fish can be determined by the development of the secondary sex characteristics in much the same way the brilliantly colored plumage is more noticeable on most male birds. We waited and watched the pin-head sized fish grow larger day by day as the weeks went by. One day the biology teacher moved all the aquariums and lights from their location alongside his desk to another room. Several days later he told me that the young fish were all beginning to look suspiciously like females, but it was still too soon to be certain. We waited approximately a month past the time the sex can normally be determined, and one evening he called me on the telephone and said he had carefully checked each fish. He couldn't believe it, but all the ones under the pink light were definitely females. This was just the opposite from what might have been expected after the results with the pumpkin flowers. We waited another ten days, and then I told a few people about this first experiment with the fish. Although this was only one incidence and could not be given any scientific significance until repeated many more times, it was interesting that all fifty fish hatched from eggs of different parents appeared to be female.

The very next day after telling these people about the fish being all female, the phone rang again, and the biology teacher was quite excited or possibly I should say upset, for now some of the fish he was certain were females were beginning to show faint signs of masculine coloration. I quickly called everyone I had told about this and tried to explain, but of course anything I said sounded rather ridiculous. We waited several weeks more, and the final results were that 80 per cent of the fish definitely turned out to be females and 20 per cent were questionable. They appeared to be males, but the development of the secondary male sex characteristics had been very materially retarded. Now it was more apparent why the biology teacher moved the lights as far away from his desk as possible. I also began to think about being on the board of directors of The North Shore Country Day School in Winnetka, Illinois, where one of my sons attended and of all the new fluorescent light fixtures that had been purchased and were waiting to be installed in the study halls. If the normal glandular development of the fish through the adolescent period could be so materially affected by different characteristics of light energy, what might be the effect upon my son? Was he predestined to become an artist or captain of the football team? Could various characteristics of light energy affect his glandular development as he grew up?

The school year ended before any more experiments with the fish could be carried on, but word of the preliminary results did reach the newspapers, and articles appeared in several magazines. As a result a letter came from a lady in New Jersey who wrote as follows:

"My sixteen year old son, who has a very keen interest in science, drew my attention to an article in a magazine regarding your experiments with light rays and their possible effect on sex determination.

"I happen to be a chinchilla breeder and at the present time I am trying to establish a sizeable herd with sufficient breeding animals to enable me to start pelting within the next few years.

"The loss of two excellent producing females in the last eight months, plus the fact that for the past three years, my few breeding animals have yielded one female and nine males prompts me to write this letter to you.

"I realize that perhaps you are not too familiar with chinchillas but females are at a premium since one good male can serve several females; thereby increasing the herd more rapidly plus cutting down on the costs of feeding, cages and space required. My interest in your experiments is more than passing, since I am in a position whereby I could benefit greatly if it were possible to produce more females than males.

"Would you advise experimenting with my breeding stock, on my own of course, as I certainly wouldn't expect you to do it? I am not interested in learning or obtaining your 'trade secrets' and if you should advise in the affirmative, I would initiate the program on my stock, only after I had consulted with my veternarian since it would be too expensive a gamble otherwise.

"Chinchillas have very dense fur and are very sensitive to extreme heat, thriving best in cool, dry temperatures of between 65-70 degrees. Even in this temperature, chinchilla books state that they can be overcome with heat if they happen to be in a cage where bright, warm sunlight strikes them through a window for several hours during the day . . .

"Right now I imagine you have concluded that there is a selfish motive behind my interest and I suppose basically I would have to admit that there is, but the majority of small ranchers are faced with the same problem as I, more or less, and are being 'held back' because they lack enough females to increase their herds rapidly.

"It is very, very discouraging to wait anxiously for three and a half months for a litter to be born only to discover that the offspring are all males. And then you wait another three and a half months and find all males again. At this stage of the business, a rancher is too small to pelt these males off and doesn't have the females to mate them with so he reaches a stalemate which puts him behind several years insofar as realizing any profits is concerned. The excess males cannot sire offspring and increase the herd, but they still require cage space and food. . . ."

I wrote back to her and asked for all the details and particulars regarding the lighting conditions of the location where she was keeping her animals. She in turn advised me that she was keeping the chinchillas in cages in a basement playroom. The room had one ceiling fixture with a regular 75-watt incandescent light and a small window at one end of the room. She also advised me that the one baby female chinchilla was from the animals in the cage at the end of the row nearest the window.

These conditions seemed to match closely the pumpkin situation except she was using ordinary incandescent light whereas I used fluorescent tubes to supplement the sunlight on the pumpkins. I promptly went to the local hardware store and purchased two 100-watt daylight incandescent bulbs and sent them to her, one to be used and one as a spare. These are the kind of bulbs with clear bluish glass that you can see through compared to the painted frosted type that makes it impossible to see the filaments.

Again the matter of waiting and wondering. Plenty of time to think over what a darn fool idea this was. I didn't want to tell anyone else about it because plenty of my friends, I felt, were already considering me a little off my orbit on the subject of light.

At last the day arrived when the postman brought another letter from the lady in New Jersey. "The blue light bulbs arrived on November seventh, and I want to thank you for them . . . The first litter just arrived on January third. I am not in the habit of handling new babies until they are a week old unless it is absolutely necessary, but yesterday I couldn't control myself any longer, and I still find it hard to believe that I found three female baby chinchillas . . ." Again this was only one isolated instance, but a very interesting one. Another matter of particular interest was that the blue lights did not arrive until somewhere between one-third and one-half way through the period of gestation. If the lights did have anything to do with the controlling of the sex of the baby chinchillas, it would indicate the controlling factor had to do primarily with the female parent. It would also indicate that the sex of the offspring could be influenced well along during the pregnancy. Several months later another letter came advising the next litter from other parents was also all females. This was doubly interesting.

Once while I was thinking about some of the unusual results that seemed to be associated with light, it suddenly occurred to me that the various growth responses that I had produced or controlled were from using different types of artificial light containing a peak of energy in specific narrow bands of wave lengths. The normal growth developments that I had prevented, such as the apple not ripening, were the result of filtering certain wave lengths from natural sunlight. This positive and negative way of acting certainly emphasized the importance of specific wave lengths of light.

Possibly a picture in one of my films might hold an answer or at least a partial explanation of all this. This is a microscopic time-lapse picture showing the streaming of the protoplasm within the cells of a living leaf of a plant. This activity goes on in connection with the process of photosynthesis in which the leaves respond to the energy of sunlight. They combine air and water with the minerals taken by the roots from the soil to create the food energy that supports all life on this earth. When the sun sets and it gets dark, this process of photosynthesis stops. It is a process of photochemistry through which chemical changes take place within the cells of the leaves of plants as they produce chlorophyl, carbohydrates, and other chemical substances. Inasmuch as light is the source of energy that brings about these different chemical changes, it then seems reasonable to assume that by changing the characteristics of the light energy that the resulting chemical changes would likewise be altered.

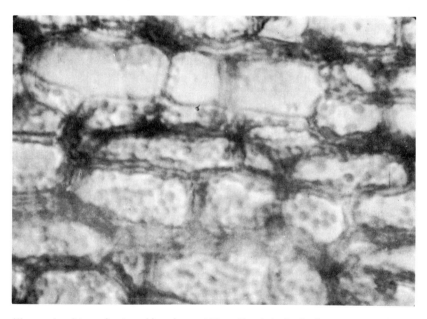

Microscopic picture showing chloroplasts within cells of leaf of plant. Energy of light activates chloroplasts and causes streaming of the protoplasm, a process that goes on in connection with photosynthesis.

This could explain the control of plant growth in response to the wave length energy of light, but how could light affect the fish and chinchillas? Here the fact that the poultry industry knows that light received through the chicken's eye stimulates the pituitary gland and increases egg production might be a very important clue. The pituitary gland is the master balance wheel of the entire glandular system, not only in chickens but other animals and humans as well. If this is so, and the entire glandular system can be affected or glandular actions modified by light received through the eye, the resulting consequences and possibilities of what this might mean are utterly fantastic. Possibly the basic principles of photochemistry in connection with the process of photosynthesis do carry over from plant life into animal life but in a greatly improved way. If the basic chemistry of the human body responds to glandular actions controlled by the pituitary gland responding to light energy, then as with plants the characteristics of the light energy would be a very important factor. Different types of light and lighting conditions ranging from natural unfiltered sunlight to various kinds of artificial light, or natural sunlight filtered through different kinds of glass, or light reflected from different colored interior decorations in a room could affect the physical well-being of an individual.

Great progress has recently been made with new types of tranquilizer drugs in helping some mental and nervous disorders. If mental illness and certain nervous disorders respond to drugs, they must be associated in some way with the chemistry of the body. If this is so and light can influence body chemistry, then this theory of light might also affect the mental as well as the physical well-being of an individual.

Two other specific films I made seem to tie into the possibility of light affecting the basic chemistry of both plants and animals. One was THE STORY OF WHEAT for the Santa Fe Railroad. It covered the growing and harvesting as well as the transportation and marketing of wheat. The other was primarily a study of tomato virus for the Wright Brothers Greenhouses in Toledo, Ohio.

As was usually the case with most productions, there were always the perplexing problems and the lighter side to each situation. The script for the film on wheat called for a scene showing a combine working in a wheat field and a freight train of grain cars going past in the background. The arm of a semaphore signal was to drop down to the horizontal position as the train passed. The people at Santa Fe headquarters had been most cooperative with the production of this film, and several of them actually accompanied me and my camera crew in a private business car that was at our disposal. Not only was the business car available to us to go anywhere on the line, but I could call for any special freight or passenger trains as needed. During the filming of this picture, several of my sons showed a sudden and keen interest in photography and wanted to help the old man even without pay. There was, however, the matter of their schooling, so I had to manage as best I could on my own.

A perfect location for the combine scene was located near Hutchinson, Kansas, in the heart of the principal wheat-producing area of the country that is served by the Santa Fe. The tracks were elevated the right amount to show off the train to best advantage. There was the semaphore signal in just the right location, and most important there were fields of golden ripe wheat as far as could be seen in all directions. The weather was clear and sunny with great big billowy clouds gently drifting by. This was exactly what I needed, all except for the combine.

As though a good fairy had waved her wand in response to a wish, there down the road on the other side of the tracks was a farmer on his combine heading our way. Unfortunately though, just as he was nearing the tracks, he turned off the road into the wheat field on the other side and began combining wheat. This was close but not the best place in order to show the signal and more important to have the sun in the right position to get the best picture. Maybe he could be persuaded to cross over into the field where we were. I went over to him and with a big smile on my face waved him down as he came by on his great big combine. He was jovial and pleasant as I explained the situation about wanting to take a picture of him combining wheat. The difficulty was that the morning sun was in the wrong position because I needed a freight train going along behind, and from this angle the shady side would be toward the camera. He said that wouldn't matter, as no freight train would be coming along those tracks before late afternoon anyway. I tried to explain that I had one with newly painted engines, and one hundred nice new grain cars waiting around the bend. All that was needed was for him to take his combine over on the other side of the tracks.

He wouldn't believe me and started to go on with his work. I persuaded him to shut off the motor and listen. Then I signaled to my head cameraman who was watching through binoculars from the far side of the field. I raised my hand and pulled on an imaginary whistle cord several times and then waited. In a few seconds back came a long loud "Toot, toot," from the compressed air horn on the diesel engine. It was interesting to see the sudden expression of surprise on the farmer's face. Without saying anything more, he started up the combine and headed for the other side of the tracks, shaking his head as he went.

We had ample time to pick out the best location where the wheat was unusually tall and thick, as the freight train had to back up several miles to get a good start in order to go by at top speed. Everything was working out perfectly according to plan. The train was going to pass the combine right in line with the signal tower. But all of a sudden the combine jammed up with wheat and stalled at the crucial moment. The farmer in his excitement had tried to cut too much of the extra thick wheat at one time. He was quite upset and very apologetic over having spoiled the picture. I told him not to worry as we would just back the train up and do it over again, and we did.

Another crucial moment in the making of this film happened one morning while photographing the activities on the floor and trading pits of the Board of Trade. At the height of the trading activity, apparently the increased load of our lights blew out the main fuse of the building in spite of our careful calculations and allowance for margin of safety. This threw everything into complete darkness and utter confusion. All the ticker tape and teletype machines stopped. Although everybody was very pleasant and understanding about the whole situation, it nevertheless was not what I would recommend as the best way to win friends and influence people.

The important incident in making the film on the story of wheat as related to the subject of light came from taking pictures of good and poor wheat. The county agent called our attention to a situation where there were two wheat fields on opposite sides of a road. They both belonged to the same farmer who had planted them at the same time with the same equip-

ment and with the same seed from the identical source purchased at the same time. One field was outstanding, and the
wheat was as good as the best anywhere in the county. It was
waist high with large full firm heads. The other was ankle-
high, and the entire field was badly infested with the wheat
virus. The field with the good wheat had recently been purchased from a neighboring farmer who had practiced some crop
rotation and had applied fertilizer to keep his land fertile. The
field with the virus had been replanted to wheat regularly for
quite a number of years without any crop rotation or application of fertilizer. There was evidence that some cattle had
strayed into this field, as wherever there was a cattle dropping,
there was also a clump of tall healthy wheat. Obviously, the
virus condition was due to a nutritional deficiency in the soil.
The county agent explained how this lowered the resistance and
made the wheat more susceptible to the virus that was thought
to be blown in from other areas or possibly carried by birds,
insects, or various other animals. There were signs of black
smut and other similar diseases on some of the wheat in spotty
patches here and there as might be expected. What impressed
me most was the uniformity of the virus right to all four corners
of the field. There was not the slightest trace of virus anywhere
to be found in the field with the healthy wheat on the other
side of the road.

The other half of this story pertains to the studies of tomato
virus. The Wright Brothers have fourteen acres of tomatoes
growing under glass in Toledo, Ohio. There are a great many
hothouse tomatoes grown in northern Ohio. The tomato virus
is one of the biggest problems growers have to contend with.
It usually appears following long periods of cloudy weather and
low sunlight intensity during the short winter days. It breaks
out even under the most sterile and carefully guarded conditions. Nevertheless, it is generally agreed that the low light level
also weakens the plants so they become more susceptible to
attack from the virus.

A virus is something, according to various definitions I have
read, that is a chemical substance lower than any form of life
capable of reproducing itself. However, it can be reproduced in
the living cells of the tissues of plants or animals. It is of a

poisonous nature and can be transmitted from one plant or animal to another. It can be isolated and crystallized as has been done with the tobacco virus and also certain human viruses.

In what little I have read about viruses, no consideration has been given to the possibility of a virus originating within the living cells of the plant itself. It seems to be generally accepted that the virus must be introduced from an outside source.

The metabolism or life itself that goes on within a living cell is the utilization of the nutritional factors present by the energy of light. The nutritional factors are like the coal or oil used for fuel to fire a boiler, and the light energy could be compared to the fire that burns it. Another comparison would be the gasoline used in an automobile engine and the spark that ignites it. If the draft in the boiler is not adjusted right or the carburetor is giving too rich a mixture, there will be incomplete combustion. This can result in both the boiler and engine giving off not only obnoxious smoke and fumes but also partially consumed fuel. In a similar way, it seems quite possible that a chemical substance of a poisonous nature could result as a by-product from an incomplete or unbalanced metabolism within the cells of a leaf. This could result from either a nutritional factor as in the case of the wheat virus or light deficiency as with the tomato virus. If so, then this chemical by-product would fit all the various descriptions of a virus. It would not be capable of reproducing itself, but if injected into the cells of other leaves, it might throw the metabolism of these cells off balance so that they would in turn produce more of the same chemical substance of a poisonous nature. It could be easily transmitted from one plant to another either by direct contact or some intermediary carrier. It could also be isolated and crystallized. It could fit all the various descriptions of a virus and still originate within the affected plant itself. This might also explain why too much plant food will kill a plant faster than not enough—simply too rich a mixture.

This is a subject I hope to investigate further. Another simple isolated experiment worth mentioning did consist of bringing some tomato plants that were badly affected with virus from a glass greenhouse to my plastic greenhouse. Ordinarily such plants are rogued out and burned immediately before the virus can spread. The plants always seem to die anyway. The interesting thing was that with just a few days of sunlight in my plastic greenhouse and a light foliar feeding of the leaves, the tomato plants quickly perked up, started new healthy growth and produced normal tomatoes. Speaking of tomatoes and harking back to the ripening of the apple, a tomato will ripen without difficulty under plastic or glass or even when picked green and kept on a shelf in a dark closet without light.

Here again was the nucleus of another highly fantastic theory. It did not tie in directly with any of the various subjects being photographed on a commercial or sponsored basis. It seemed to be just one more crackpot idea to be added to the list. Nevertheless it was very intriguing, and again I decided to stick my neck out and dust off the ledger sheet for the experimental and experience account, as this is where the expense would have to be charged. To take pictures that would show what I wanted to study required building additional time-lapse equipment specially designed for taking microscopic pictures. This new unit was designed to take microscopic time-lapse pictures of the streaming of the protoplasm within the cell of a leaf as stimulated by direct unfiltered sunlight as contrasted with various types of artificial light illumination.

The temperature of the subject being photographed could be controlled from 0° to 250° Fahrenheit. A secondary optical system was designed to superimpose an image of an electronic thermometer recording the temperature so that it would show simultaneously with the picture of the subject. In this way it would be possible to show precisely the effect of different sources of light and variations of temperature on the photo-chemistry that goes on in connection with the process of photosynthesis within the cells of a leaf. It would then be possible to study the effect on the germination of spores, mitosis of cells and other growth processes.

This new time-lapse microscopic unit was quite a gadget to be classified in the basement hobby category, and fortunately it could be used to take other microscopic pictures in which more interest was continuing to develop on the part of commercial sponsors principally for advertising purposes. However, it does open up a whole new avenue of approach for new time-lapse studies.

Chapter 12

The Darkest Hour

The increasing demand for time-lapse pictures necessitated building a mezzanine floor in the plastic greenhouse and installing additional cameras. More and more bits of interesting information were turning up at a much faster rate. All in all everything was beginning to run more smoothly except for two major problems. First, no one would pay any serious attention to the medical research possibilities of my time-lapse films. Secondly, advancing arthritis in my hip was making it increasingly difficult to carry a projector around for lectures or even to go up and down the basement stairs. Several doctors had recommended wearing a large metal brace and advised a plastic hip joint would be necessary before very long. As a result my wife and I were seriously considering moving to a house on one floor in order to avoid the stairs. But the time-lapse studio created a real problem, for this would be extremely difficult and costly to move. Meanwhile two lecture trips took me to Florida during two successive winters. While there I spent as much time as possible on the beach to find out if basking in the sun would possibly help my arthritis. There were many stories about arthritis being affected by weather, but much as I would have liked a good excuse to spend more time in Florida during the winter, I could honestly not notice the slightest benefit. Sometimes it actually felt worse. On one trip I drove the family down and back. I enjoyed driving in the country, but my arthritis was always noticeably more aggravated at the end of the day regardless of how comfortable and relaxing the driver's seat might be. Nerves and fatigue, said the doctors. I should relax more. But how could I relax more than sitting in the sun on the beach. Furthermore, while driving the car or sitting on the beach, I was always extra careful to wear my dark glasses to avoid any eye strain, as my eyes were very sensitive to the bright sunlight.

The only other times my arthritis definitely seemed to noticeably bother me more was immediately after my regular weekly
TV program and following the filming of it which was done the
next day in the converted garage studio. Here maybe I could
agree with the doctors about nerves and fatigue, but some extra
aspirin would usually help considerably. Other than this, it
was not possible to correlate my arthritic discomfort with anything else, including diet. Many well-wishing friends brought
various remedies, tonics, and vitamin pills that had cured some
distant relative. My arthritis must have been of a different variety, as none helped at all. Hot baths were relaxing but of no
real value. Injections of various new glandular extracts would
increase the discomfort for the first day or two and then give
only four or five days' relief. Then the arthritis would be right
back again. A cane helped a great deal by relieving some of the
weight from my hip, but after using it for over two years, my
elbow began to give trouble. I rode a bicycle around the yard
back and forth between the house, tool shed and greenhouse. It
was a girl's bicycle because it was easier to get on. However,
this was rather humiliating as far as some of the children were
concerned, and I usually tried to stay out of sight when any of
their friends were present. They thought I could at least ride a
boy's bicycle. There were times when my other hip and knee
also felt rather uncomfortable.

The problem of what to do was becoming more acute, when
one day I happened to break my glasses. While waiting for a
new pair to be made, I wore my spares in the interim. The nose
piece was a little tight and bothered me, so I took them off most
of the time. The weather had been nice for several days, and
there was some light work outside that I was doing as best I
could with my cane in one hand. Suddenly I didn't seem to need
the cane. My elbow was fine and my hip was not bothering me
much even though I hadn't taken any extra amount of aspirin.
It was hard to figure out why my arthritis should all of a sudden be so much better. My hip hadn't felt this well for three
or four years. I began walking back and forth on the driveway.
Fifteen minutes went by, and I must have walked a mile. I ran
into the house and up the stairs two at a time to tell my wife.
She had been watching me out the window and worrying. Had
I lost my cane again, and why all the walking back and forth

and around in circles without my glasses. It was shortly before Christmas, and if she would hurry and finish her Christmas shopping, we could go to Florida for a week between TV programs. I wanted to sit in the sun again without any glasses. In three days we were on a plane headed south, and my wife was quite relieved that all I wanted to take off was my glasses while sitting in the sun.

During that week the weather was very cold so it was not possible to be on the beach in a bathing suit. In fact, an overcoat was necessary the entire time. Nevertheless, it was possible to be outdoors in the natural sunlight all day without any glasses. Perhaps this was a good thing because the light intensity away from the beach was not as great and made it much easier to do without dark glasses. At all times I was careful not to strain my eyes from too much light and never looked directly at the sun unless it was quite hazy or a little cloudy. I was also careful to guard against sunburn. Much of the time was spent sitting under a palm tree where I could read or look out into the open and still receive the benefits of natural sunlight as contrasted to artificial light or sunlight filtered through glass. Fortunately, I was able to read without my glasses and needed them primarily for distant vision. My particular reason for not wearing dark glasses was that in addition to the glass itself filtering out virtually all the ultraviolet and certain other shorter wave lengths of sunlight energy, the characteristics of the light are further changed depending on the color of the glass. This acts as a filter restricting the transmission of all the other colors or wave lengths and transmits a peak of energy of the particular wave length of whatever color the glass happens to be. While in the hotel, it was a great temptation to look out through a big picture window at the tropical vegetation and beautiful blue ocean. Conscientiously though, I avoided looking through the window glass and also did as little driving as possible so as not to have to look through an automobile windshield. I avoided bright artificial lights and did not watch television or go to the movies.

The effect on my arthritis was as beneficial as an injection of one of the glandular extracts right into the hip joint but without the intervening day or two of increased discomfort. There was no doubt about it. My arthritis was definitely much better, and I was satisfied it was not imagination or wishful thinking. Furthermore, after several days of not wearing glasses at all, my eyes were no longer so extra sensitive to the bright sunlight even on the beach. Before the week was up, I played several rounds of golf on a short nine-hole course and went walking on the beach without my cane. I felt like a new person.

Theories may be interesting to think about and discuss with other people, but this was affecting my own arthritis, a much more personal and realistic matter. Theories or no theories, wishful thinking or plain imagination, my arthritis was very much better, and this was wonderful. Maybe I was one of the lucky people you hear about who get better for no reason at all, but I felt strongly that there was a reason. I had taken my glasses off and let the full unfiltered natural sunlight energy into my eyes and had also made a point of being outdoors six hours or more each day whether or not it was sunny or cloudy. To me the results were convincing enough that light received through the eyes must stimulate the pituitary or some other gland such as the pineal gland about which not too much is known.

The pineal gland is present in all craniate vertebrate animals. It is thought to be a remnant of an important sense organ utilized to a greater extent by more primitive animals. It is in most cases located at the base of the brain, but with some fish and reptiles and especially certain lizards, it is raised near the upper surface of the head and has the structure of an eye with a more or less distinct retina and lens. It is then called the pineal eye. At any rate, something was stimulating the glands that lubricated my joints without artificially injecting any of the prepared glandular extracts.

Back home I continued to stay outdoors every day without my glasses as much as possible from before sunrise until after sunset in spite of cold or cloudy weather. I used a small blue Christmas tree light as a night light in the bathroom just in case momentarily interrupting the dark night period or human sleep with bright artificial light might possibly have some detrimental or adverse effect on human beings as it definitely did with so many different plants. I moved my office from a room in the basement that had nothing but artificial light to a corner of my plastic greenhouse. When it was warm enough to be outside, I did as much office work as possible right out in the open. I also went swimming a great deal or otherwise wore a bathing suit as much as possible. Some benefit from the sun is unquestionably absorbed through the skin. With a little careful planning, the rehearsal time for my live weekly television show was cut to a minimum, and the bright studio lights were turned off between rehearsal time and air time. I also began using more time-lapse pictures in order to shorten the live portion of the program during which time it was necessary to be under the very bright artificial lights, especially those required for color television. The film series of my programs had also recently been completed. For over a year I had spent almost two full days each week under the bright studio lights in order to repeat my weekly television program so that it could be recorded on color film. The total number of hours under the intense studio lights was therefore cut from approximately sixteen a week to forty minutes at the most. This in itself made a tremendous difference, but even so, my arthritis still noticeably bothered me after each television program or driving a car for any considerable distance and looking through the glass windshield.

The reactions were very positive. Several friends who had arthritis tried the same experiment and had similar beneficial results. Other friends with a variety of ailments including bursitis, ulcers, acne and bleeding gums insisted they were helped. This sounded worse than the claims made for some of the old-fashioned cure-all patent medicines. On the other hand, could there conceivably be any similarity in the type of weakness of the tissues that cause bleeding gums and weak spindly growth of plants that do not receive sufficient sunlight? Could it be possible that there might be any further similarity between the basic weakness of the cell structure in the tissues that causes bleeding gums and the weakness in tissue of other parts of the body such as the brain or the heart itself?

Theoretically, if this theory of light energy affecting the basic body chemistry is right, then it might go even much further as far as being responsible for various ailments and diseases, particularly of the old age or degenerative type, but all this needs further extensive study before any positive statements can be made. Another friend no longer was bothered with hay fever. Could not wearing glasses and being out in the sunlight possibly bring about a change in the body chemistry so the grains of pollen remained dormant?

One day I met a man who had previously taken a number of still photographs for me. He had meanwhile been on an assignment that required an intense amount of artificial lighting in large interior areas. He was an extreme diabetic and while on this job had a severe attack of his diabetes which resulted in the bursting of some blood vessels in the retina of both eyes. As a result he became almost totally blind and could just distinguish the difference between day and night. He had been in this condition for approximately four years during which time he had numerous additional blood vessels burst in his eyes. He continued to work for the same company but in the photographic dark room where he was put in charge of processing film. Between batches of film he would occupy his time by reading Braille—in the dark.

The day I saw him again and learned of his blindness, I told of my experience with arthritis. Arrangements were made with his boss for a table outside where he could read his Braille while waiting for films to be processed. He made an effort to be outdoors as much as possible while at home. Now approximately six months later, he has not had a single blood vessel burst, can distinguish different colors, and can see enough to follow the vague outline of the sidewalk ahead as he walks to work. Another single isolated case but a very interesting one to follow. Incidentally, he always wore thick, strong glasses before going blind.

Some doctors have said cancer is a virus or at least in some way associated with it. If this is so, then the possibility of influencing body chemistry by the characteristics of the light energy received through the eye might conceivably be an important factor in the metabolism of the individual cells of the tissues of the body. The same principles of nutritional factors, light energy, and a balanced metabolism would follow the same line of reasoning as with both the wheat and tomato viruses.

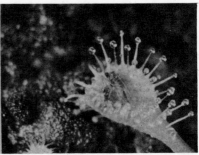

Mosquito caught in sticky substance at end of tendril of sundew plant.

Tendrils pass mosquito toward center of leaf.

Leaf curls around mosquito and se-cretes more digestive juices. Leaf of sundew plant requires approximately one hour to curl around insect which is held firmly in droplets of sticky fluid.

After day or two leaf opens again, and tendrils discard first insect. An-other mosquito has been caught by tendrils in lower right hand portion of picture and will be passed to the center of the leaf.

Just exactly how this energy could be transmitted was hard to visualize. Nevertheless, I had photographed plants that could transmit energy or impulses quite rapidly, and certainly these plants have no nervous system anything like that of animals or humans. Both the venus fly trap and sundew plants are good examples, but even better possibly would be the *Mimosa pudica* or sensitive-plant. An interesting characteristic of this plant is that it folds its leaves tightly together when it gets dark and seems to actually go to sleep at night. It opens its leaves again during the daytime. If you touch the leaves with your finger or strike them with any object, they quickly fold up in a matter of approximately one second. If the plant is left undisturbed, the leaves will slowly open again in approximately five or ten minutes. If the tip end of a leaf is singed with the flame of a match, the shock is greater, and the reaction can be seen as it travels throughout the entire plant. The singed leaf first folds up quickly, then the branch collapses. The shock wave travels in a matter of approximately one or two seconds through the main stem to the other branches which collapse. Then the shock continues to travel through these other branches to the leaves that finally fold up. Again if the plant is not disturbed, the leaves will slowly open in approximately ten minutes time. A further interesting phenomenon is that the entire plant can be anesthetized with ordinary ether so that it will not react even to the more severe shock of singeing a leaf with the flame of a match. This may be done by placing some cotton saturated with ether near the plant and covering it over with an air-tight cover. When the cover is removed and the plant has been in the open fresh air again for ten or fifteen minutes, it will react in its normal way. Another interesting observation regarding the sensitive-plant is that even though it is kept in total darkness in the basement under a concrete ceiling as well as the usual concrete walls, the leaves continue to open and close according to the outdoor daylight or night periods. Whether or not this reaction is controlled by cosmic rays or other radiant energy forces capable of penetrating concrete or not is somewhat of a mystery.

The fact remains that these plants are capable of transmitting this energy or shock impulse in a way that is not fully understood. Therefore, it seems reasonable that light energy or the effects of it could be similarly transmitted through animal tissue and become an important factor in the metabolic function of the individual cells.

I showed my pictures and stressed the effects of light and its important possibilities to a number of medical groups, universities and the research personnel of seven large pharmaceutical companies across the country. Same reaction every time. Excellent pictures, very interesting, and somebody would be getting in touch with me for giving the matter further thought. But nothing ever happened. One company wanted to test out the

Leaves of the mimosa plant normally open during daytime period.

The leaves fold together and branches droop slightly during night time.

Leaves will quickly fold up and branches collapse if struck with solid object or singed with the flame of a match. See picture to right.

This picture shows leaf in folded position and branch collapsing as the result of singeing tip end of leaf.

Mimosa plant can be anesthetized by pouring ether on cotton and covering with air tight box with glass front.

Plant will show no response to singeing from flame while under effects of ether. Will respond in usual way again after being in fresh air for approximately fifteen minutes.

theory of spores in connection with the common cold but was unable to find anyone with a cold at the right time after searching for six months in the New York City area. Another company was very interested in helping with some of my projects until I suggested they also help by sharing some of the expenses. This abruptly changed their attitude. I showed my pictures and told my story at the headquarters of the United States Department of Agriculture, Public Health Institute, and Surgeon General's Office of the Army, all at my own expense, but could stir up no action. Finally the United States Information Agency became interested and translated the most recent and complete magazine article about my work into Russian and sent it to Moscow. I tried to interest several of the large foundations, but no results. Two universities did make an appeal for a research grant based on time-lapse photography that I would do jointly with them, but were turned down cold.

The research departments of several large corporations did show some interest in the possibilities of time-lapse photography. However, their interest was only in its application to particular problems on which they were already working. Any thought of further investigating some of my observations about light beyond its effect on plant growth was too radical to be worthy of any consideration. The heads of the research departments of two large corporations confidentially expressed some interest but frankly said any official recognition or participation in such an outlandish idea would subject them to the risk of possible ridicule by other scientists. It might react unfavorably on the reputation and standing of their companies. Invariably they would all check the available literature on the subject and report there was nothing to support my observations. What information was in the literature dealt primarily with color therapy and the psychological effect of different colors on more or less emotionally unstable people. This was no help at all and only tended to further classify me in the category of psychosomatic crackpots. It is certainly a commendable practice to check the literature to learn what information is available or even to find out what the generally accepted theories are on a particular subject. The fact though that no information exists certainly is no proof that a new theory is wrong to start with. Sometimes new information disproves old established theories.

In conducting experiments on any new theory, it is important not to accept negative results on preliminary tests too quickly as being conclusive. Sometimes a minor variation of no apparent importance may accidentally prove to be the cause for some basically sound reasoning not proving out under laboratory conditions.

Nobody realized better than I that to scientifically prove any of my casual observations would require a large clinical laboratory with specialists in many fields, a full medical staff, and a thousand or more patients with complete hospital facilities. Then the results of many experiments could be tabulated, and any significant findings further investigated. Such suggestions were quite numerous and all very well but called for facilities far beyond anything in my basement time-lapse studio.

Although all the concrete walls in my basement time-lapse studio had originally been painted white to make it look as much as possible like a scientific laboratory, the paint was beginning to turn a yellowish color. Possibly it looked a little dingy to some people. Accordingly, I renamed it my ivory cellar and gave it a fresh coat of ivory paint.

The progress was slow and discouraging. At times the whole idea seemed utterly ridiculous even to me, and often quite hopeless. Many times I pinned my hopes on a particular showing of my films for some official recognition and acceptance of the importance of light energy and other interesting phenomena revealed through my time-lapse pictures. Many times there was always the same polite but negative response. Several senior educators and top doctors suggested quite frankly that I should forget about any medical application or reference in connection with light, particularly concerning cancer, before I brought too much ridicule and disgrace not only upon myself but my family as well. This was certainly a time when I wished I might be able to reach up and pull an imaginary whistle cord and hear a "Toot, toot" off in the distance.

Chapter 13
"Toot, Toot"

There was no imaginary whistle cord, but at last one day things began to happen that were tremendously helpful. The Chicago Technical Societies Council honored me with one of their annual Merit Awards, "for outstanding technical achievements, service to science, fellow scientists and the community." Soon afterwards Loyola University in Chicago conferred upon me an honorary degree of Doctor of Science. Next I was asked to become a member of the faculty in the Biology Department, and very soon after this I was also made a member of the faculty of Michigan State University in the Department of Horticulture. Meanwhile members of the faculty of other universities including Harvard, Illinois, Iowa, Northwestern, Purdue and Wisconsin cooperated whole-heartedly with me in an advisory capacity with the production of various technical films for a number of nationally known large corporations. The Chicago Horticultural Society awarded me the Charles L. Hutchinson Medal for my "time-lapse work in horticulture and contributions to the scientific knowledge of plant growth." All these associations helped tremendously in lending scientific dignity to what started in my basement "ivory tower."

The idea of using time-lapse photography for more than purely entertainment and advertising films was taking hold. Additional experiments were started by others at both Loyola and Michigan State Universities. One of the most encouraging and gratifying experiences came when the Lamp Development Department of the General Electric Company retained me as a consultant to study and advise on the effects of radiant energy on plants and animals. The Quaker Oats Company placed their research farm near Barrington, Illinois, at our disposal. Experiments were started in subjecting chickens and various domestic animals to different types of lighting conditions. The Quaker Oats Farm was otherwise used primarily for testing various animal feed formulas. This was a tremendous help, as the animals and also people experienced in handling and caring for them, plus all their past records and case histories were already

established as a well organized and operating farm. To dupli-
cate such a set-up would have been not only very costly but also
would require years to gain the necessary knowledge and
experience.

   More recently I have built two time-lapse camera units for
use in the Cancer Research Program at Chas. Pfizer and Co.,
Inc. They have retained me to consult with them on time-lapse
problems and the manner in which they relate to my own work.
Other important companies have also indicated an interest in
this subject of the importance of the full spectrum of sunlight
energy, and a number of exciting experiments are either already
started or in the definite planning stage. These experiments
may take several years to complete and will undoubtedly lead
to other experiments requiring additional years. This raises the
question as to whether or not the best policy would be to keep
all information strictly confidential and release nothing until
scientifically proven beyond any doubt. On the other hand, it
is my firm belief that by making as much information available
with caution as possible that others may possess information
that might supply the missing pieces to the overall puzzle. As
mentioned in the preface, I have already put off the writing of
this book over thirty years. If it were to be delayed until everything that has been discussed is finally proved or disproved in
whole or in part, I am afraid this would not be during the
remainder of my lifetime.

   Meanwhile more and more bits of interesting information
keep turning up from the most unexpected sources. On one of
my regular television programs, I was privileged to have Warden
Joseph E. Ragen of the Illinois State Penitentiary as my guest.
His work in the rehabilitation of men at Stateville Penitentiary
and the importance of horticultural therapy had been written
up in one of the Chicago newspapers. This sounded most interesting, so I contacted Warden Ragen and was invited to see the
prison gardens and work being done along these lines inside the
prison walls. The extent of the gardens and their beauty was
simply amazing. The fact that the men did all the work and
raised the plants themselves was certainly commendable but
their obvious enthusiasm and feeling of personal pride in their
work was what impressed me the most. Warden Ragen showed

me many letters received from men after their release as well as letters received from men still at Stateville that might be summed up by the remarks of one man who came there as one of the toughest criminals and psychological problems ever to be dealt with. Warden Ragen told me he had stopped one day and asked this man how he was getting along. The man straightened up, pointed to the flower bed he had just finished cultivating and said:

> "Warden, this is the first decent thing I have accomplished in my life. I've been a thief and criminal all my life. All my gains were ill-gotten, and I find now I can accomplish something that will be worthwhile, not only for myself, but for people as a whole. I know flowers are not only pretty, but they are profitable as well. I am sure that when my sentence is served, you will never hear from me again so far as crime is concerned. I am going to ask you to help me find employment in a greenhouse or as a gardener."

From later correspondence I had with Warden Ragen, I again quote from one of his letters as follows:

"I should like to say one thing, and one which can possibly be considered repetitious on my part. I am positive that schools for delinquents, reformatories and prisons are not the proper place to make good citizens. I do not think that children are instinctively born criminals. I believe they are led into lives of crime in many instances, by delinquent parents, improper home situations, lack of love and care to which they are entitled as children and lack of religious, academic and vocational training. Certainly, if our prison populations are to be reduced, we must do more about the 'cause' which produces the delinquent child of today. He must be guided through his formative years on the road to good citizenship rather than be permitted to drift to a life of crime and disgrace, and further, become a very expensive liability to taxpayers and society in general."

Certainly working with flowers and plants in the garden close to nature is a very good psychological influence. Possibly being out in the sunlight as contrasted to the solitary confinement in a dark or artificially lighted cell is even more basically a good thing, too. If it is basically the natural sunlight received through the eyes that is beneficial in helping to rehabilitate such men, then it might also be an important factor with regard to the much discussed subject of the rate of increase of juvenile delinquency. In my mind it raises the question about the ultimate effect on human health and normal growth development resulting from excessive exposure to other than natural sunlight as the result of increased and extensive use of large picture windows, glass buildings, and modern brighter artificial lighting. The fad of wearing dark glasses is sweeping the country. The matter of driving or being driven in an automobile to school or work is becoming more important all the time. Many outdoor sports are now attended at night under the lights or watched over TV. The importance of education is being stressed more and more, and students are working harder and longer under the midnight electricity to meet the stiffer requirements and increased competition. New mental institutions, hospitals and especially maternity wards where newly born infants get their first glimpse of light have larger windows that are no longer made to open and more and brighter artificial lights.

If light energy is associated with cancer or certain other physical and mental disorders, then the question might be raised as to the comparative cancer rate of people still living under primitive conditions with those in more highly industrialized nations. Unfortunately, what statistics are available regarding primitive people are the hardest to find and unquestionably the most unreliable. Nevertheless, John Gunther mentions in his book, "INSIDE AFRICA," that "Africa has malaria, tuberculosis, leprosy, syphilis, elephantiasis, yaws. Cancer is, however, almost unknown among Africans . . . but the worst African disease is something more prosaic than we have already mentioned, malnutrition."

A check of the records of one of the large hospitals in Chicago indicates that the rate of cancer with the Negro people of that city is just as high as with white people. The almost total absence of cancer amongst the native people of Central Africa could be due to some other factor such as diet. However, if diet were primarily responsible and was closely tied in with cancer, then the cancer rate might be expected to be higher in those areas where malnutrition is such a major problem.

It is not the purpose of this book to give medical advice but rather to record interesting observations that have come about as the result of a hobby of taking time-lapse pictures. Anyone interested in experimenting on his own should consult his or her doctor first. Fortunately, the theory of the importance of the full spectrum of sunlight energy does not involve the taking of any untried or unproven medicines or drugs that might be toxic or otherwise harmful. It does not mean that present drugs or medicines being taken must be discontinued. As a matter of fact, in my own case I found that in the past taking vitamins seemed to cause canker sores in my mouth and minor eruptions or blemishes of the skin. After I began making a point of being outdoors in the sunlight without my glasses, the taking of vitamins proved most helpful and beneficial. This would seem to tie in again to the matter of a balanced metabolism and the importance of a good sensible well balanced diet in relation to the light energy factor.

Another isolated incident more on the humorous side but still of a personal nature, was that during the worst of my arthritis my children also began calling me baldy. They had good reason for doing so, as the hair on the top of my head was rapidly becoming rather scarce. However, this situation also corrected itself after I began staying outdoors without my glasses. This made me think of the poor mink with the heavy winter fur all summer.

For several years I had been bothered more and more with common head colds and a sore throat. Several people who regularly watched my TV program either sent me or recommended various cough remedies that seemed to have little effect. This troublesome condition also disappeared as I continued to practice my theories of being outdoors in the natural sunlight. For some time I more or less joked with various friends including some in the medical profession about feeling so much better, and all agreed wholeheartedly that it was a wonderful thing regardless of whether it was due purely to my imagination or not.

After six months of not wearing glasses except for what little driving of the car was absolutely essential and for focusing my projector when showing pictures, I began to notice that wearing my glasses even for these short periods seemed to strain my eyes more and more. Accordingly, an appointment with my oculist for a regular check-up seemed advisable. This time it was necessary to go back for a second examination which my doctor explained was customary in order to double check any such drastic change as was the case with the condition of my eyes. The principal difference in my new prescription was that the rather strong prisms previously needed to correct a muscular weakness were no longer at all needed. With this encouragement, I decided also to have my hip x-rayed again. It was most gratifying to have my doctor advise that the x-ray pictures showed a definite strengthening and improvement in the area of my hip joint that had been causing so much trouble. A physical examination revealed the complete disappearance of a 30 per cent restriction of the movement or rotation of the hip joint which my doctor commented on as being wonderful but quite surprising and most unusual to say the least. For six months I had been imagining I felt better, and it was a great relief to have these x-ray pictures and examination confirm my imagination.

If the theory of the importance of the full spectrum of sunlight energy proves to be true, it will necessitate some changes in our present way of living. However, it certainly will not mean that everybody will have to go back to living in caves or grass huts. It will mean using certain types of plastic or glass that will permit the transmission of ultraviolet and shorter wave lengths of light energy. Unfortunately at the present time the trend on the part of manufacturers of plastic has been to add a substance that stops the transmission of ultraviolet light so that the light transmission qualities of plastic will be as nearly like glass as possible. This substance also reduces the deterioration of plastic from ultra-violet radiation. It will also mean that artificial lights will have to be developed that more closely give off the same distribution of wave length energy as natural sunlight. This should not be too difficult a task to accomplish, and present light blubs would then be replaced with the new ones. In this regard it should be pointed out that present day so-called sun lamps give off a high concentration of energy in the ultra-violet range of the spectrum, and most man-ufacturers caution against looking directly at the light.

It will mean the reappraisment of the possible usefulness of such glands and organs of the body as the appendix, tonsils, adenoids, gall bladder, and others often removed with the thought of good riddance when there has been something wrong with any of them.

New interest and enthusiasm should be stimulated in all out-door activities and sports. It should emphasize the importance of such organizations as the Boy Scouts, Girl Scouts, Campfire Girls, Isaac Walton League and others devoted to outdoor activi-ties. It should encourage people to be outdoors as much as pos-sible and without eye glasses or dark glasses. Some companies might even want to consider changing the regular working hours in order to lengthen the lunch period and permit employees to get outdoors during the daylight hours, particularly during the winter season. The general attitude toward walking a mile or more to school or to work may change so that such a walk could be looked on as a pleasure rather than a terrific hardship. More people may find it fun to eat their meals on an open porch or use the back yard barbecue. Winter vacations for people living in colder climates will undoubtedly become less undesirable, par-ticularly if it is possible to go to the sunny southland for a mid-winter outdoor break. It should not be too difficult to find many more ways for outdoor living.

The theory of the importance of the full spectrum of sunlight energy, I believe, gives additional meaning to the opening verses of the BIBLE, for when God said, "Let there be light," the refer-ence was unquestionably to sunlight.

LECTURES
given by
JOHN OTT

ALABAMA
Birmingham — Garden Club

CALIFORNIA
Burbank — Walt Disney Studios
Pasadena — California Institute of Technology
— Garden Club
Santa Barbara and Montecito — Garden Club — 2 times

COLORADO
Colorado Springs — Garden Club
Denver — Colorado Forestry & Horticulture Assn. — 2 times
Grand Junction — Western Colorado Horticultural Society

CONNECTICUT
Bridgeport — General Electric Company
Bristol — Mount Holyoke Alumnae
Darien and Stamford — Women's Garden Club
Farmington — Garden Club
Litchfield — Garden Club
New Canaan — Garden Club and Bird Protective Society
Washington — Garden Club

DELAWARE
Wilmington — Garden Club

DISTRICT OF COLUMBIA
Washington — Garden Club
— International Photographic Exposition
— National Geographic Society
— Office of Surgeon General U. S. Army
— U. S. Public Health Institute

FLORIDA
Daytona Beach — Halifax Country Garden Club
Jacksonville — Men's Garden Club
Miami — Fairchild Gardens — 3 times
Miami Beach — Garden Club
Palm Beach — Garden Club — 2 times

Sarasota — Garden Club
    — Founders Circle, Women's Garden Club

GEORGIA
Atlanta — Peachtree Garden Club
Columbus — United Garden Clubs
Savannah — Men's Garden Club

IDAHO
Farragut Naval Training Station

ILLINOIS
Addison — Brookwood Country Club
Aurora — Men's Garden Club
Barrington — Garden Club — 2 times
    — Women's Club — 2 times
Belvidere — Woman's Club
Blue Island — Lutheran Church
Champaign — Anhydrous Ammonia Institute
Chicago — All School Council, Foreman High School — 2 times
    Alpha Chi Sigma Fraternity (Chicago Professional Chapter of Chemists)
American Cancer Society
American Chemical Society—Chicago Section—2 times
American Dry Milk Institute
American Electroplaters' Society, Chicago Branch
American Institute of Banking, Chicago Chapter
American Nature Study Society
American Society for Horticultural Science
American Society for Testing Materials
American Society of Medical Technologists
Area Camera Clubs Assn. (ARCA Club)
Armour Research Foundation
Arthe Club
Artist Guild
Association of Elementary Assistant Principals
Bell & Howell Company
Bell & Howell Company — Pioneer Club
Billings Club
Biological Photographic Association
Building Managers' Association of Chicago

Casino Club
Central Scientific Company, Employees' Meeting
Central States Dahlia Society
Chicago Academy of Sciences — 3 times
Chicago Aquarium Society
Chicago Allergy Society
Chicago Engineers Club
Chicago Horticultural Society — 3 times
Chicago Scientific Film Society
Commonwealth Edison Company (Edison Camera Club)
Commonwealth Edison Company — Inter-Co. Engineering Conference
Conference of Club Presidents and Program Chairmen — 3 times
Contemporary Club of Chicago
Marshall Field & Company — Advertising Department
4-H Club — 2 times
Fortnightly Club of Chicago — 2 times
Garden Club of Illinois — 2 times
Garden Club of America
Illinois Committee, Chicago Assoc. of Com.
Illinois Institute of Technology — Alumni Assn.
Illinois State Nurserymen's Assn.
Illinois State Park Commissioners
International Harvester Company
International Photographers of the Motion Picture Industries, Local 666
Junior League of Chicago
Loyola University, Sigma Xi
Museum of Science and Industry
Natural History Museum
North American Gladiolus Council
Physics Club of Chicago
Rotary Club of Chicago — 2 times
Saint Chrysostom's Church — 2 times
Salomon Brothers & Hutzler — 2 times
Society of American Florists & Ornamental Horticulturists
Society of Motion Picture Engineers — 2 times

Society of Motion Picture and Television Engineers
Standard Club
State Florists' Association
South Shore Country Club
Union League Club — 3 times
University of Illinois — 3 times
White Elephant Rummage Shop
Wildwood Garden Club
Woman's Athletic Club of Chicago
Woman's Club — Beverly Hills
Woman's Club — Hamilton Park
Woman's Club — Irving Park
Woman's Neighborhood Club of Rogers Park
Chicago Heights — Business Women's Club
Clarendon Hills — Garden Club — 3 times
Danville — Garden Club
Decatur — Garden Club
Deerfield — Woman's Club
Downers Grove — Men's Garden Club
Elgin — Men's Garden Club
Elmhurst — Women's Garden Club
Evanston — Evanston Hospital Medical Seminar
          North End Men's Club — 2 times
          Northwestern University Guild
          Northwestern University School of Speech
          Northwestern University, Sigma Xi
          Senior Board of Infant Welfare
          University Club of Evanston — 2 times
Flossmoor — Garden Club
Freeport — Men's Garden Club
Geneva — Women's Garden Club — 2 times
Glen Ellyn — Women's Garden Club
Glencoe — Men's Club, The Methodist Church
          North Shore Garden Club
          Village Gardeners
Glenview — Women's Garden Club
Highland Park — Highland Park Men's Garden Club
              Highland Park PTA
              Presbyterian Church Men's Club
Hinsdale — Woman's Club

Joliet — Gardeners of the Woman's Club
Kenilworth — Garden Club — 2 times
La Grange — First Congregational Church — Men's Club
    La Grange Chemists' Club
Lake Bluff — Garden Club
Lake Forest — Lake Forest Day School
    Men's Garden Club
    North Shore Horticulture Society — 2 times
    School Children
LaSalle — Illinois Valley Garden Club
Lisle — The Morton Arboretum
Lombard — Garden Club
    Regional Meeting of State Park Commissioners
North Chicago — Abbot Laboratories — 2 times
Oak Park — Men's Club — First Congregational Church
    19th Century Women's Club
    Tea Cup Circle
    Women's Guild, First Baptist Church
Park Ridge — Garden Club
    Park Ridge School for Girls
    Park Ridge University Club
Pekin — Association of Commerce
    Community High School
Peoria — Knife & Fork Club
Ravinia — Garden Club
River Forest — Tennis Club
Riverside — Woman's Club
Rockford — Employees Dinner J. L. Clark Manufacturing Company
    Men's Garden Club
    Woman's Club
Techny — Mission Gardens
Urbana — College of Christian Life
    Illinois State Florists' Association
    University of Illinois
    Waukegan — Elks' Club
    Wheaton — Women's Garden Club
    Wilmette — Garden Club
    Winnetka — Book Club
        Business & Professional Women's Club
        Christ Church — 5 times
        Faith, Hope and Charity Guild

Garden Club — 3 times
Izaak Walton League — 2 times
Mills College Committee
New Trier High School — 2 times
North Shore Country Day School — 4 times
Rotary Club — 2 times
Woman's Club — Garden Department
Woodley Road Women's Club
Woodstock — Men's Garden Club
Zion — Lyceum Course

INDIANA
Culver — Culver Military Academy
Elkhart — Miles Laboratories
Ft. Wayne — Northeastern Indiana Section American Chemical Society
Gary — Kiwanis Club
Hammond — School Teachers Convention
Indianapolis — Garden Club of Indiana Convention
Indiana State Teachers' Assn., Nature Study Section
Terre Haute — Nature Study Department, Woman's Club
Lafayette — Purdue University — 2 times
Whiting — Whiting Science Club

IOWA
Ames — Iowa State College, Iowa Horticultural Society
Davenport — Tri-City Garden Club

KENTUCKY
Lexington — Garden Club — 2 times
National Council of State Garden Clubs Convention
Louisville — Smith College Club of Kentucky

LOUISIANA
Natchitoches — Women's Garden Club

MAINE
Mt. Desert Island — Garden Club
Portland — Garden Club

MARYLAND
  Baltimore — Garden Club
          Medical Group
          School
          Vegetable Growers' Assn. of America, National Convention
  Beltsville — U. S. Agr. Experimental Station, Bureau of Plant Industry — 2 times

MASSACHUSETTS
  Boston — Massachusetts Horticultural Society — 6 times
          Men's Garden Clubs of America Convention
          North Shore Garden Club — 2 times
  Cohasset — Garden Club
  Hingham — Derby Academy
  Lenox — Garden Club
  Marblehead — Garden Club
  Martha's Vineyard — West Chop
  New Bedford — Garden Club
  Newton Centre — Woman's Club
  Orleans — Woman's Club
  Setauket — North Suffolk Garden Club
  Waban — Woman's Club
  Wellesley Hills — Woman's Club
  Worcester — Clark University Biology Department & Botanical Society
          Garden Club
          Worcester County Horticultural Society

MICHIGAN
  Battle Creek — Garden Club
  Benton Harbor — Federated Garden Clubs of Michigan
                Indian Hills Garden Club — 2 times
  Detroit — Detroit Academy of Medicine
          Michigan Nurserymen's Association
  East Lansing — Michigan Landscape Conference — 2 times
              Michigan State University — 4 times
  Grand Rapids — Kent Garden Club
              Kiwanis Club
  Grosse Pointe — Joint Meeting of Garden Clubs
  Kalamazoo — Hardy Perennial Garden Club

MINNESOTA
Minneapolis — Men's Garden Club
St. Paul — Garden Club
Wayzetta — Lake Minnetonka Garden Club

MISSISSIPPI
Jackson— Men's Garden Club

MISSOURI
Cape Girardeau — Federated Garden Clubs of Missouri Convention
Jefferson City — Missouri Farm Bureau Federation
Kansas City — Garden Club
St. Louis — Garden Club
    National Peach Council
    Photographic Society of America
    Women's Club

NEBRASKA
Omaha — Ad-Sell League of Omaha

NEW JERSEY
Maywood — John L. Smith Memorial for Cancer Research
Montclair — Garden Club
Plainfield — Garden Club
Rahway — Merck and Co., Inc. — 2 times
Rumson — Garden Club

NEW MEXICO
Santa Fe — Okalaya Garden Club — 2 times

NEW YORK
Albany — Garden Club
Brooklyn — Chas. Pfizer & Co., Inc. — 2 times
Chautauqua — Chautauqua Association
East Hampton — Garden Club
Milbrook — Garden Club
New York — Memorial Hospital
    Garden Club of America
Oyster Bay — North Country Garden Club
Rochester — Garden Club — 2 times
    Memorial Art Gallery

New York State Seed Association
Society of Motion Picture & Television Engineers
Roslyn — North Country Garden Club
Rye — Garden Club
Setauket — North Suffolk Garden Club
West Hampton Beach — Garden Club

NORTH CAROLINA
Charlotte — Garden Club
Winston-Salem — Council of Garden Clubs

OHIO
Cleveland — Garden Center of Greater Cleveland — 4 times
Columbus — Franklin Garden Club
              Ohio Association of Garden Clubs
Dayton — Univis Lens Company
Lakeside — Lakeside Yard and Garden Club
Marysville — O. M. Scott & Sons Company
Nela Park — General Electric Company — 3 times
Tiffin — Tiffin Civic Forum
        Tiffin Columbian High School
Toledo — Ohio State Horticultural Society
        Ohio Vegetable & Potato Growers' Association
        Rotary Club — 2 times
        YMCA
        Zoological Society

OKLAHOMA
Tulsa — Southwestern Art Association

PENNSYLVANIA
Philadelphia — The Academy of Natural Sciences — 2 times
        State Fish and Game Protective Association
        Rohm and Haas Company
Pittsburgh — Garden Club of Allegheny County

RHODE ISLAND
Newport — Garden Club
Providence — Garden Club

TENNESSEE
  Knoxville — University of Tennessee
  Lookout Mountain — Garden Club
  Nashville — Garden Club

TEXAS
  Dallas — Garden Club
  Ft. Worth — Garden Club
              School Children
  Houston — Garden Club

VIRGINIA
  Richmond — James River Garden Club
  Williamsburg — Garden Symposium Colonial Williamsburg — 2
    times

WASHINGTON
  Spokane — Associated Garden Clubs
              St. Nicholas Guild, Cathedral of St. John

WEST VIRGINIA
  White Sulphur Springs — American Plant Food Institute — 2 times
                          West Virginia State Garden Club

WISCONSIN
  Kohler — Woman's Club
  Lake Geneva — Garden Club
                Wisconsin Garden Club Federation
  Madison — University of Wisconsin — 3 times
              Presbyterian Church — 2 times
  Milwaukee — Rotary Club
              Salomon Bros. & Hutzler
  Racine — Woman's Club

HAWAII
  Honolulu — Second World Orchid Conference

CANADA
  Toronto — National Shade Tree Conference
              Ontario Fruit & Vegetable Growers' Assn.
              Royal Canadian Institute

ENGLAND
  London — Horticultural Club, Royal Horticultural Society Newhall
  Grantchester — Town hall
  Cambridge — University

SCOTLAND
  Edinburgh — University group, Royal Botanic Gardens

FRANCE
  Gif-sur Yvette — National Center for Scientific Research
  Paris — Faculty of Sciences, La Sorbonne

AUSTRALIA
  Sydney — Private showing

SOUTH AFRICA
  Durban — Tourist group

SOUTH AMERICA
  Buenos Aires — Photographic Symposium

SINGAPORE — Private showing